Penguin Books
Dossier 51

Gilles Perrault, who was born in Paris in 1931,
worked as a solicitor for several years before
doing military service in Algeria. *The
Parachutists*, based on his experiences there,
won him the first *Prix d'Aujourd'hui*, awarded
in 1962. Two years later his *Secret of D-Day*
became an international best-seller. His next
book, *The Red Orchestra*, sold over 120,000
copies in France, and was translated into
half a dozen languages. *Dossier 51*, his first
novel, has already been published to great
acclaim in France, Germany, Italy and Portugal.
Gilles Perrault lives with his wife and family
in a tiny village in Normandy facing the
historic Utah Beach, up which the soldiers of
the Fourth US Division swarmed on 6 June 1944.

Gilles Perrault

Dossier 51
An Entertainment
Translated by Douglas Parmée

Penguin Books

Penguin Books Ltd, Harmondsworth,
Middlesex, England
Penguin Books Australia Ltd, Ringwood,
Victoria, Australia

First published in France 1969
Published in Great Britain by Weidenfeld & Nicolson Ltd 1971
Published in Penguin Books 1973

Made and printed in Great Britain by
Hunt Barnard Printing Ltd, Aylesbury
Set in Monotype Times

To Thérèse

Date: 11.9.1967   Classification: R
From: Mercury   Ref. no. 1974 ND
To: Minerva
Subject: O.R.V.A.

Jean de Malarielle, Minister Plenipotentiary, Department of Foreign Affairs, has been appointed French Ambassador in Copenhagen.

He will be replaced at O.R.V.A. by Dominique Auphal, at present Chief Under-Secretary, Department of Technical Co-operation.

Dominique Auphal will take up his duties on 16.10.1967.

Source: 8274

7

Date: 12.9.1967   Classification: TS
From: Minerva   Ref. no. 1975 PS
To:Mercury
Subject: 51

1) Obtain all information concerning Dominique Auphal.
2) Submit a list of all Jean de Malarielle's staff who will be continuing to work at O.R.V.A.
3) Submit a list of all staff that Auphal will be taking with him.
4) Inform whether Auphal's family will be accompanying him and
5) Whether he will be occupying the official accommodation vacated by Malarielle.
6) Auphal is allotted code no. 51.

Date: 12.9.1967   Classification: R
From: Minerva   Ref. no. 1976 PL
To: Clio
Subject: Request for records

The file of Auphal, Dominique

Date: 12.9.1967   Classification: TS
From: Clio   Ref. no. 1977 LQ
To: Minerva
Subject: Request for records

In reply to your request of today's date, please find herewith the file of Auphal, Dominique, and 7 (seven) appendices.

AUPHAL, Dominique

1. *Family*

Born 31.3.1931 in Paris (VI), son of Lucien, born 15.8.1890 in Bordeaux (Gironde), doctor, died 13.2.1961 and of Monique de Servas, born 12.12.1905 at Bourges (Cher), occupation housewife.

Married 12.11.1958 Liliane de Maupertain, born 15.9.1938 at Maupertain (Manche), daughter of Robert, born 8.6.1902 at Maupertain (Manche), farmer, and of Sabine Martin, born 16.10.1915 at Quettehou (Manche), occupation housewife.

Two children:

Stéphane, born 30.8.1959 in Madrid (Spain)

Elodie, born 1.10.1964 in Rabat (Morocco)

2. *Education*

Primary education at the Ecole Saint-Patrice, 8 Rue Cassette, Paris (VI)

Secondary education at the Collège Ladislas, 19 Rue de Fleurus, Paris (VI)

Institut d'Etudes Politiques (1949-1952)

Ecole Nationale d'Administration (1953–1955)

Degrees and other qualifications:

Baccalauréat (Arts and Philosophy)

Diploma of the Institut d'Etudes Politiques (Public Service Dept)

3. *Military Service*

Graded fit for Armed Forces by Military Service Board in 1950

Deferred under art. 23 on 27.12.1950 by Regional Director of Recruiting and Statistics (1st Region)

Called up with class 1955–2B

Posted to 24th I.T.R., 1st T.C. Despatched to unit 21.10.1955, joined unit 22.10.1955

Service calculated as from 15.10.1955

Transferred to Reserve Officers Training at Cherchell on 4.4.1956. Despatched to unit 6.4.1956. Joined unit 9.4.1956

Promoted officer cadet 17.7.1956

Posted to 117th I.R. 9.8.1956. Despatched to unit 14.8.1956. Joined unit 15.8.1956

Promoted 2nd lieutenant, 13.1.1957

Sent home on demobilization leave 17.1.1958 to 15.2.1958

Formally demobilized 16.2.1958. Retained on list of Reserve Officers as from that date

Decorations:
  Military Cross
  Commemorative Medal for active service in the maintenance of law and order in Algeria

Wounds: Nil

4. *Career*

1.3.1958	Secretary, Diplomatic Service, grade 2, Central Office, Department of Technical Co-operation
1.3.1959	Secretary, Diplomatic Service, grade 3
9.7.1959	Appointed Second Secretary in the Madrid Embassy
1.3.1961	Secretary, Diplomatic Service, grade 4
16.4.1962	Appointed First Secretary in the Stockholm Embassy
1.3.1963	Secretary, Diplomatic Service, grade 5
19.5.1964	Appointed First Secretary in the Rabat Embassy
1.3.1965	Secretary, Diplomatic Service, grade 6
5.2.1966	Appointed Head of Central Office, Department of Technical Co-operation
1.3.1967	Secretary, Diplomatic Service, grade 7

Appendix 1

Extract from 'Die Spinne' Organigram (1948)
Uruguay, Montevideo, 9, calle Colon, Ferrero Francesco, alias
Bergman, alias Auphal (or Anphal): missing since 26.8.1947
    U.D. 15.1.1953: Ferrero Julio (?) died 20.7.1950 at Fray Bentos
                    (Uruguay)
Requested Charon for D.I. 19.6.1953. Nil return. FF 18.9.1959
(See also under Anphal Louis, ref. Clio 198.932)

Appendix 2

Extract from Dido Report 8163 CP of 28.3.1951

... The demonstration was banned. However, at about 1800 hrs two or three thousand former deportees assembled in front of the Opera, chanting: 'No Nazis in Paris' and 'We want peace'. 504 people were arrested, bringing the total number of those questioned between 24.1.1951 (Hotel Astoria) and 15.2.1951 (Opera) up to 3,767.

Herewith list of names of above:

Dermoy, Michel, lawyer, born 9.4.1923 in Paris (XVI), son of Marcel and Josépha Schneider, residing 143 Rue Leconte de Lisle, Paris (XVI)

(See also under Cambernon, Georgie, married name Dermoy, died 14.5.1948, ref. Clio 689.223)

U.D.: On 1.2.1960, Dermoy, Michel, married as his second wife Geneviève de Maupertain, born at Maupertain (Manche) on 15.12.1936, daughter of Robert and Sabine Martin, secretary, sister of Liliane de Maupertain, wife of Auphal, Dominique (see also under Auphal, Dominique, Clio 904.822)

Appendix 3

AUPHAL, Liliane

Liliane de Maupertain, wife of Auphal, Dominique, born 15.9.1938 at Maupertain (Manche), daughter of Robert, born 8.6.1902 at Maupertain (Manche), farmer, and of Martin, Sabine, 16.10.1915 at Quettehou (Manche), no occupation.

Primary education at the local elementary school at Maupertain (Manche)

Secondary education at the Lycée Jussieu in Cherbourg (Manche) Baccalauréat (1st part, Arts)

Interpreters' School (English), 18 Square Boucicaut, Paris (VII)

Married on 12.11.1958 Auphal, Dominique, born 31.3.1931 in Paris (VI), son of Lucien, born 15.8.1890, in Bordeaux (Gironde), doctor, died 13.2.1961, and of Monique de Servas, born 12.12. 1905, at Bourges (Cher), no occupation.

Two children:

Stéphane, born 30.8.1959 in Madrid (Spain)

Elodie, born 1.10.1964 in Rabat (Morocco)

Occupation: housewife

Appendix 4

Extract from Report 4023 BJ of 30.4.1961 by 6930
... M. Geoffroy de Lancelet, First Counsellor of the French
Embassy, today left Madrid for Paris to communicate to the
Minister of Foreign Affairs the Spanish Government's reply to
representations made by the French Government as a result of
the departure for Algeria of General Salan and Captain Ferrandi.
M. Geoffroy de Lancelet was accompanied by the Second
Secretary, M. Dominique Auphal.

Appendix 5

AUPHAL, Monique
  Maiden name: de Servas
  Mother of Auphal, Dominique, First Secretary at the French
Embassy at Rabat (see also Clio 904.822)
  Residing at 82 Rue Guynemer, Paris (VI)
  No occupation

  Convicted on 24.5.1964 at the Pontoise (Seine) Quarter Sessions of manslaughter and driving whilst under the influence of
alcohol. Fined 8,000 francs and given a suspended sentence of
six months' imprisonment. Banned from driving for three years.

Appendix 6

Report 4322 JM of 15.8.1965 made by 4923
Auphal, Liliane, wife of Auphal, Dominique, First Secretary at
the French Embassy in Rabat, is the mistress of Comi, Giuseppe,
Cultural Attaché at the Italian Embassy in Rabat. The affair is
alleged to have started some months ago. The couple meet at
Comi's villa, 94 Allée Césareo, on Tuesdays and Fridays in the
early afternoon.

Auphal, Dominique, seems unaware of this affair.

Appendix 7

Report 7300 DB of 4.6.1967 by Pericles
The French diplomat Auphal, Frédéric, arrived in Beirut at 0915 hrs on 2.6.1967 (PANAM Flight 813)

He went from the airport straight to the French Embassy

He left the French Embassy at 2030 hrs on 3.6.1967 and went straight to the airport. He took off at 2152 hrs for home and Paris (BOAC Flight 417)

Auphal, Frédéric, is not known. Request for I.R. to 8274 on 20.7.1967. Reply of 21.9.1967 states that Auphal, Frédéric, might be identical with Auphal, Dominique (see also Clio 904.822)

Date: 2.10.1967
From: Mercury
To: Minerva
Subject: 51

Classification: TS
Ref. no. 1986 MD

Further to your memo 1975 PS of 12.9.1967
1) Re 51, see Md attached
2) All of Jean de Malarielle's staff will be staying on with the exception of his secretary Jeanne Loursais, who is retiring
3) No staff have as yet been earmarked to accompany 51
4) 51's family will be joining him but probably not until some later date
5) It has not yet been possible to ascertain whether 51 and his family will be occupying the official residence vacated by Jean de Malarielle.

Source: 8274

51's appointment to O.R.V.A. has come as a surprise only to those who are still unaware of his connection with the Prime Minister's entourage. As a fellow-student and contemporary at the E.N.A. (Ecole Nationale d'Administration) of Georges Chéron (formerly P.P.S. to the Prime Minister and later promoted Secretary of State in the recent reshuffle) 51 was certainly helped by this friendship at the time of his difficulties during his period of service in Rabat. Since his appointment as head of the central office at the Department of Technical Co-operation at the Quai d'Orsay, he has had eighteen months of completely untroubled tenure of office. He is reputed to be a strong supporter of present French foreign policy. At the time of the recent disturbances in the Middle East, he undertook a confidential mission to Damascus. He is said to have contemplated standing as a candidate in the 1967 General Elections and is supposed to have been dissuaded from this course by the Minister of Foreign Affairs in person. His appointment to such an important post as O.R.V.A. suggests that the Minister may have taken the opportunity then to give him to understand that he is destined for high diplomatic office and that entering Parliament would have been the equivalent of forsaking the substance for the shadow.

Source: 8274

Date: 2.10.1967   Classification: TS
From: Minerva   Ref. no. 1987 DM
To: Mercury
Subject: 51

You have failed to understand the first para. of our memo 1975
PS of 12.9.1967.

We repeat:
'Obtain *all* information concerning Dominique Auphal.'

Date: 3.10.1967
From: Mercury
To: Minerva
Subject: 51

Classification: TS
Ref. no. 1988 AG

1. IN RE YOUR MEMO 1987 DM OF 2.10.1967

A. We wish to point out that, contrary to your statement, the terms of the above memo are not identical with those of your memo 1975 PS of 12.9.1967. In your most recent memo the word *all* is underlined, which was not the case in the previous memo of 12.9.1967. We wish formally to protest against this procedure of modifying on successive dates the form of a service memo purporting to be identical.

B. We note that in your memo of 2.10.1967 you make use both of a first and of a family name whereas you had specified in your memo of 12.9.1967 that these should be replaced by the code no. 51. We would draw your attention to articles 425 and 426 of the regulations governing internal administration:

'Article 425. Any spoken reference by the use of a first name to a person having been allotted a pseudonym or code-number constitutes a first degree infringement punishable under article 832. Any written use of such a name constitutes a second degree infringement, punishable under article 833.

'Article 426. Any spoken reference by use of a family name to a person having been allotted a pseudonym or code-number constitutes a third degree infringement punishable under article 834. Any written use of such a family name constitutes a fourth degree infringement punishable under article 835.'

2. IN RE THE SUBSTANCE OF THE ABOVE MEMO

In his directive J 4114 of 2.1.1966, Jupiter specifically states that political reasons of overriding importance render the greatest caution necessary in any operations involving France. A supplementary directive J 4812 of 15.3.1966 gives a list of a number of current operations which were to be cancelled in accordance with the terms of the general directive. Since that date not only has no order been received modifying the above-mentioned instructions but Mercury has on various occasions received verbal confirmation of them.

It is likely that the French security services will have placed 51 under a screen of protection and observation as soon as his appointment to O.R.V.A. was announced. Any detailed intensive intelligence operation on 51 is liable to attract the attention of these security services, thus giving rise to those difficulties which Jupiter's directive enjoins us to avoid.

In consequence, Mercury will carry out the instructions contained in para. 1 of your memo of 12.9.1967 and repeated, with modifications, in your memo of 2.10.1967 only on receipt of express instructions from Jupiter himself.

Copy for information to Jupiter

Date: 4.10.1967   Classification: TS
From: Minerva   Ref. no. 1989 MG
To: Jupiter
Subject: O.R.V.A.

Since its inception, all our attempts to infiltrate O.R.V.A. through its French members have proved abortive. This failure is the more to be regretted, since the importance of O.R.V.A. has steadily increased in these five years, so that this organization has become the king-pin of French policy towards developing countries. O.R.V.A., which ranked as a C 2 objective five years ago, is now classified as A1.

This objective forms part of Mercury's commitments. Mercury has never found itself in a position to supply us with positive intelligence data concerning Jean de Malarielle. Any information that has been gathered has been superficial and unfailingly negative, with the implied suggestion that the person concerned was not a suitable subject for exploitation. This is but one example amongst many of a Utopian conception of mankind that seems to have dominated Mercury's thinking for some time past.

Jean de Malarielle's replacement by Dominique Auphal makes a further attempt possible. Experience has shown that French political and diplomatic staff are eminently suitable for exploitation. It would be surprising should O.R.V.A. have the good fortune to receive from this source only those who are impervious to this process.

Minerva is not unmindful of Jupiter's directive of 2.1.1966. Caution is not, however, the same thing as inaction. If the attempt to obtain information about France *is liable* to give rise to difficulties, it is *certain* that lack of knowledge of French plans would give rise to even greater difficulties.

Further, Minerva wishes to protest against Mercury's claim to be allowed to decide for itself whether or not it is appropriate to obey instructions. Mercury's function is strictly executive. Minerva expresses the hope that Jupiter may wish to remind Mercury that its task is to collect intelligence on such objectives as may be assigned to it without any discussion of the value of these objectives, any such assessment being Minerva's sole responsibility.

It is quite plain that O.R.V.A. will continue to elude us if Mercury confines itself to transmitting information such as contained in its memo 1986 Md, which is merely a rehash of various articles published in the Paris press at the time of Auphal's appointment.

Date: 4.10.1967
From: Jupiter
To: Mercury
Subject: 51

Classification: TS
Ref. no. J 5376

Mercury will carry out Minerva's instructions as laid down in para. 1 of its memo 1975 PS of 12.9.1967 and repeated, in modified form, in its memo 1987 DM of 2.10.1967.

Mercury will bear in mind directive J 4114 of 2.1.1966 and avoid any action liable to give rise to difficulties with the French security services.

Copy for information to Minerva

Date: 5.10.1967
From: Minerva
To: Mercury
Subject: 51

Classification: TS
Ref. no. 1990 GP

1) 51 takes up his duties on 16th inst. You will set up an appropriate intelligence agency in the town in which he is going to reside

2) This town will be allotted the code-name Delphi. The organization which 51 is joining will be known by the code-name Parthenon

3) Immediately after 51's departure from Paris, his wife will be placed under observation by means of intermittent shadowing and reports on her activities

4) 51's wife will receive code-number 52. Code-number 53 is allotted to his son and 54 to his daughter

5) You are to discover the identity of the secretary who will replace Jeanne Loursais (who is retiring) at the Parthenon.

1. Herewith 19 items numbered 1 to 19:

   1) Note on 51's way of life.
   2) Typescript of recorded conversation between Marie Marguerite (51's domestic servant) and 8956 (27.10.1967).
   3) Copy of part of a letter sent by 51 to 52 on 28.10.1967.
   4) Handwritten note from 51 to 5353 dated 30.10.1967 (original).
   5) Report on shadowing of 52 (25.10.1967).
   6) Report on shadowing of 52 (28.10.1967).
   7) Photocopy of a letter sent by 51 to 53 on 31.10.1967.
   8) List of identity papers and other documents in 51's wallet as on 2.11.1967.
   9) Note on 51's attitude in Rabat at the time of the Ben Barka affair.
   10) Memorandum relating to Item 11.
   11) Photograph of 51 in Rabat.
   12) Memorandum relating to item 13.
   13) Photograph of 52 in Rabat.
   14) Memorandum relating to items 15 to 19.
   15
   to   Photographs of 51 in Delphi, of 52, 53, and 54 in Paris,
   19   and of 52's sister and Philippe Lescarre in Paris.

2. Jeanne Loursais has been replaced by Sylvia Mouriac who commenced work on 16.10.1967 (Source: 8274).

3. 51 took up his duties on the same date.

29

4. He is occupying the official accommodation vacated by his predecessor.
5. His family will join him at a date yet to be fixed (cf. item 4).

Item 1 (Note on 51's way of life)

51 and family occupy a five-room flat at 31 Avenue de l'Observatoire, Paris (VI). The monthly rental is 900 francs, plus charges.

They have one domestic servant, Marie Marguerite, born at Maupertain (Manche) on 15.1.1947. Her wages are 250 francs per month, which is lower than the normal Paris rate.

Their car is a 1965 Peugot 404, costing at that time (new) approximately 10,000 francs.

They own no other flat or house.

51 buys his suits ready-made at Arny's in the Rue de Sèvres. 52 has her clothes made by a private dress-maker, Magda Filanges, but she sometimes shops elsewhere. For the last three years, in the spring, she has bought a tailor-made costume from Chanel's. She has her hair done once a week at Jean Peyrole's, in the Boulevard de Magenta.

51 and 52 give a dinner party once a week, usually on Wednesdays. There are rarely more than four guests. They hold a big At Home once a year, when they use a caterer.

In 1964, they spent ten days at Courchevel; in 1965, eight days at Verbier (Switzerland) and in 1966, ten days at Val d'Isère. They always take these holidays in February.

They spend their summer holidays at Maupertain Manor, in the Cotentin peninsula, the residence of 52's parents.

51's salary while in Rabat was of the order of 5,000 francs per month, including all allowances. As these diplomatic foreign

31

allowances were discontinued as soon as he returned to Paris, his salary fell to 2,544 francs per month.

His present salary is not known. As a guide, his predecessor at the Parthenon received 11,000 francs per month approximately, but in view of 51's lower seniority he is probably receiving appreciably less.

Sources: Marie Marguerite via 8956
8274

Item 2 (Typescript of recorded conversation between Marie Marguerite (51's domestic servant) and 8956, on 27.10.1967)

8956	So you get on O.K. with the boss and his wife
M.M.	Not so bad/the bind is they know my old mum and dad because I come from Maupertain same as she does/so when I want to go out in the 'evening' I've got to get back by one or else they'll kick up a fuss with my old man
8956	Speak a bit louder can you/I can't hear what you're saying
M.M.	It's that lousy orchestra that's playing too loud/I told you I didn't want to come here/for one thing I only like slow dances/all this wriggling about on one spot gets on my wick
8956	And so he keeps chasing you all the time
M.M.	He's not like that/he's a cold fish if you ask me/always prim and proper but he never looks at you as if you was human/I bet his Liliane doesn't get much fun out of him
8956	Perhaps she gets it from someone else
M.M.	That's her business (One sentence drowned by background music)
8956	Do you like champagne/waiter we'll have some champagne

Unidentified voice	Very good sir
M.M.	My goodness you must be rolling in it
8956	It's because I think you're rather sweet/I hope we can get to know each other really well
M.M.	Switch it off lovie/unless you've got the ring handy/I say that's a tango/shall we have a go (32 seconds silence)
M.M.	Do you recognize it
8956	Sweethearts from Auvergne isn't it
M.M.	Yes with verschuren/him and jouvin are my favourites/once they stuck up notices all over Maupertain saying georges jouvin and his golden trumpet was going to come for the August 15th holiday but it didn't come off/I say look at that boy with the curly hair the little one on the left who's pretending not to see me/can you see him/on the left I said/he often comes to the rue d'odessa to dance/he asked me to dance once/I don't mind telling you he was an expert at the old follow through/ had me almost sitting across his leg he did/you dance close up but not like him/well in the end I said to him straight out that's it I said the first time and the last O.K., so don't try any more funny business or I'll give you something you won't forget in a hurry/I tell you if he'd said a word I'd have socked him one good and proper
8956	That's going it a bit strong isn't it wanting to sock someone/did you learn that from the boss
M.M.	Being socked one you mean/if you think I'd let anyone sock me/I've been nearly two years in Paris don't forget
8956	That's not what I meant/I meant that perhaps your boss and the missus sometimes had a bit of plate throwing when they had a row
M.M.	What on earth are you nattering about/everything's all diplomatic with them/when the master gets in a temper he's all toffee-nosed and his mouth goes all tight/now she might be a bit more hot-blooded/you

34

can see her going all white but she never shouts she can hold herself back that bitch/and for crying out loud shut up about the pair of them will you/and now the tango's finished and we've been talking all the time that's smart isn't it/let me tell you something/if you think that

(ends)

Comment: The above conversation was recorded during the second meeting between 8956 and Marie Marguerite. 8956 reports that at the end of this second meeting the subject became very reticent and failed to appear as arranged for the third meeting. We shall request 8956 to endeavour to re-establish contact with the subject if you issue formal instructions to that effect.

Item 3 (Copy of part of a letter sent by 51 to 52 on 28.10.1967)

My dear one,

The parcel has arrived in fair condition. Thank you for the note you enclosed with it. Perhaps you forgot that Post Office regulations don't allow letters to be sent with a parcel. Fortunately everything was all right and I didn't have to pay any surcharge. Don't forget to settle up with Métivier.

Things are beginning to take shape. Dear old Malarielle certainly was one of the old school. I shall have some amusing stories to tell you about his attitude towards our underdeveloped friends. Suffice it to say that his haughty ways – which are going to seem quite astounding at the Danish court – often appeared most strange to these very deserving people. I've begun by tackling the French-speaking community. But most unfortunately for me, because I'm not very fond of them, a good number of the French-speakers here are Negroes ('he's seeing everything in black' your dear father would have said at this point – and we should all have 'split our sides with laughter'!) I've been striking a realistic note with them, frank and down-to-earth, in a word, the complete technocrat and, whatever the topic of conversation, I try to bring in 'computers'. They're all the more impressed because most of them are lawyers or Arts men and so technocracy is just a wonderful dream for them.

I've been in touch with our Embassy. Carquebut pointed out, not without a certain asperity, that for a Secretary who's only in grade seven my appointment was a very nice bit of promotion. The poor man knows that he's in a dead end. That's his bad luck. He's one of those thoroughly detestable diplomats who for years have been French *and* American Ambassadors. You know what I mean. All the same, I confess that I shall feel much happier when I'm finally made up to Second Counsellor. Another two years to go. Had the pleasure of meeting that nice man Jean Maurvier again – I was at the Quai d'Orsay with him in 1958. He hasn't changed. Still as affected and precious as ever. We'll have the privilege of listening to his sentimental verse whispered in sugary tones . . . All the same, he's a first-rate cultural attaché.

The villa's quite reasonable. It can't compare with 'Simoun', of course, but we knew that it would be a long time before we should get anything as nice as Rabat. An eminently residential district. A small garden to make up for the Luxembourg Gardens. A lot of space. Well laid-out. A dab of paint in the drawing-room and a thorough clean-out of the bedrooms and everything will be splendid. They've used up all this year's maintenance grants but I'll ask the Quai for a special allocation in advance from next year's grant if need be.

When are you going to come out? Up till now, I've managed to refuse the inevitable invitations on various pretexts (work, finding my feet, settling-in and so on) but I don't see how I shall be able to escape the official receptions which will certainly be on their way shortly. Remember Rabat. Even if I don't soon find a way of solving the problem of Stéphane, I still think you ought to come out here fairly soon.

Has Hervé rung up? He's really too bad. You wait. Simone will turn out to have been right in the end . . . I must confess to being a trifle disappointed, aren't you?

I must have sounded rather strange on the phone. It's because my secretary happened to be in my office. She's twenty-eight and seems a competent young woman – she's already proved herself an excellent shorthand-typist. As far as her looks go, I suppose you might call her pretty but I won't go into details for fear of provoking your rather special sense of humour . . .

I'll stop now and finish this letter off tomorrow after the post has arrived. If there's a letter from you then I'll be able to answer any of your queries.

Source and remarks:
1) The text of this letter was copied and passed on to us by 5353
2) 5353 used to work for 51's predecessor and 51 has kept her on. She arrives at the villa at about 0830 hrs every day and leaves it at about 1300 hrs. We would remind you that 5353's results have been consistently rather poor
3) 5353 succeeded in having access to the letter because after writing it, 51 left it on his writing-pad where 5353 discovered it whilst cleaning. 51 finished the letter off at lunch-time and took it away with him

Item 4 (Original handwritten note from 51 to 5353, dated 30.10.1967)

I shan't be back for lunch. If Mr N'Diombe rings, tell him I shall be in my office from 3 o'clock (1500 hrs) onwards. Don't forget to pick up my blue suit from the cleaners. Thank you.

Item 5 (Report on shadowing of 52)

25 Oct. 1967

1148 hrs (8025) 52 left the block of flats at 31 Avenue de l'Observatoire and got into a radio-taxi (7527 SV 75) which had been waiting for some minutes. 52 was dressed in a green coat and fawn leather boots

(8047) Rue Auguste Comte, Rue d'Assas, Boulevard Raspail, Boulevard Saint-Germain, Quai d'Orsay, down along the Seine, Pont d'Iéna, Avenue des Nations-Unies, Avenue d'Iéna, Rue Bossière, Place Victor-Hugo, Avenue Malakoff, Rue Duret

1211 hrs (8047) 52 got out of the taxi and went into the block of flats at 4 Rue Duret

1427 hrs (8025) 52 came out of the block of flats at 4 Rue Duret together with a woman. Description: height about 5′ 5″; hair, brown; complexion, mat. Dressed in a flared white coat

Rue Duret, Avenue de la Grande-Armée

52 and the dark woman got into an Austin-Cooper S (6424 RN 75) parked in the side-avenue of the Avenue de la Grande-Armée

1518 hrs (8047) The Austin-Cooper parked on the pedestrian crossing at the junction of the Rue Saint-

Guillaume and Rue de Grenelle

(8016) Rue de la Chaise, Boulevard Raspail, Rue de Sèvres

(8016) 52 and the dark woman went into the dress-shop 'Eva', 18, Rue de Sèvres

1638 hrs (8016) 52 and the dark woman left the shop carrying parcels. They kissed each other. The dark woman went off in the direction of the junction of Boulevard Raspail and the Rue de Sèvres. 52 stopped a taxi (1470 QD 75)

1731 hrs (8025) 52 got out of a taxi (3295 TR 75) and went into the block of flats at 31, Avenue de l'Observatoire

1738 hrs (8025) 52 left the building and got back into the taxi

(8047) Rue Auguste-Comte, Rue Guynemer, Rue Bonaparte, Rue Jacob, Rue de l'Université

1749 hrs (8047) 52 went into a block of flats at 29C Rue de l'Université

1852 hrs (8025) 52 left the block 29C Rue de l'Université in a yellow Lotus Europa (9870 TV 75) driven by a man

2001 hrs (8025) 52 appeared at the window of her flat at 31 Avenue de l'Observatoire

(8025) 52 disappeared

Remarks:
1) On investigation, the woman visited by 52 at 4 Rue Duret, is her sister, Geneviève de Maupertain, wife of Michel Dermoy, lawyer
2) The man visited by 52 on 25 and 28.10.1967 has been identified as Philippe Lescarre, 40 years of age, bachelor, Deputy Managing Director, Compagnie Française des Alliages

Item 6 (Report on shadowing of 52)

28 Oct. 1967

1702 hrs	(8025)	52 left the building at 31, Avenue de l'Observatoire and took a radio-taxi (4579 VF 75) which arrived at that moment
	(8047)	Rue Auguste-Comte, Rue Guynemer, Rue Bonaparte, Rue Jacob, Rue de l'Université
1720 hrs	(8047)	52 entered the block of flats at 29C Rue de l'Université
	(8016)	52 rang at the door of the third-floor flat. The door was opened. A man's voice said: 'You're early again, dammit'. The door was closed
2102 hrs	(8025)	52 left the building at 29C Rue de l'Université in a yellow Lotus Europa (9870 TV 75) driven by a man. Description: hair, black, curly; complexion, tanned. Dressed in a grey coat
	(8047)	Rue de l'Université, Boulevard Raspail, Place de la Concorde
0020 hrs	(8025)	The Lotus dropped 52 in front of the block of flats at 31 Avenue de l'Observatoire. 52 and the man exchanged a few words. 52 went into the building

Item 7 (Photocopy of a letter from 51 to 53 dated 31.10.1967)

My own little Stevie,

Here's a letter from Daddy. Would you like to make him feel happy? Then sit down on your pouf, put Abel away out of sight and make Cain read this letter right through to the end.

Are you ready? Then here we go.

I had a very funny dream last night. I dreamt that Madame Marcelle was getting bigger and bigger, really enormous, so enormous that she finally floated up into the air like that balloon we once saw on the telly, do you remember, with the old gentleman who was throwing sand overboard? (and Lolo thought it was Nanny's sandman! Don't tell Mummy, will you, but I think girls are a bit silly, don't you?) Anyway, in my dream Madame Marcelle was going up and up and Monsieur Honoré was trying to hold her down by her feet. But he couldn't manage it and so in the end he gave a shout and let her go and she started to go right up to the sky . . . Fortunately there were the trees in the avenue! She got stuck between two branches, just opposite the fourth floor. As she was crying and Monsieur Honoré kept on shouting louder and louder, all the tenants ran to their windows. And do you know what happened next? Madame d'Etchandart started shouting that Madame Marcelle had floated up on purpose to spy on her and that she ought to have been satisfied at just listening at her door! As a matter of fact, everybody was sorry for poor Madame Marcelle who kept on hitting against the branches of

43

the tree. Down below, Monsieur Honoré was crying so hard that the gutter in the street was almost running over, so much so that the roadsweeper (you know, the man who is black all over and smells horrid) came up and shouted that if he didn't stop the whole district would be flooded. Everyone was yelling and Mummy put cottonwool in her ears the way she does when she can't sleep and then suddenly, what do you think they heard? Ting-a-ling! Ting-a-ling! The firemen with their bell! Monsieur Nauvois had sent for them. They dashed up with their great big ladder the way they did when they came and saved Madame Marcelle's little pussy when he had got stuck up the chestnut-tree.

I don't know what happened in the end, because at that moment I woke up. But what a business! You must write and tell me quickly if Madame Marcelle is still the same size as ever or whether she's grown as big as she was in my dream. I keep on wondering all the time and it stops me working.

I hope Cain isn't too tired? And I hope Abel is still hidden out of sight! No cheating, now! I hope too that you've not been taking advantage of my being away to go drinking in the evening! That wouldn't be a good boy. Now that I've gone away and you're the only man left at home, you must be even more grown-up, look after Mummy and Lolo and don't make Margot cross.

I'm busy trying to find a school for you here that will be as nice as Madame Valérie's. As soon as I've found one you shall come out with Mummy, Lolo and Margot and we shall all be happy together as we were before.

That's all for now. You can let Abel out of his hiding-place. Best wishes and a big kiss for Cain.

See you soon my darling little Stevie,

Daddy

P.S. Do you know something that would make me a very happy Daddy? Copy out my letter and be careful not to get the letters wrong and then send it to me. If you haven't got more than five things wrong, I'll buy you a no. 6 Meccano set!

Source and remarks:
The above letter was photocopied in the following circumstances:

44

On 31.10.1967, on arriving at work, 5353 saw a cream-coloured car of unidentified make parked in front of 51's house, chauffeur-driven, with a passenger in the back-seat. It was not the normal office car provided by the French Embassy in Delphi for 51's use. 51 was just finishing breakfast. As soon as 5353 appeared, he left the table, informed her that he was going away for the day and asked her to post a sealed envelope containing the above letter.

As 5353's weekly meeting with 5672 was due to take place that same evening, 5353 decided that she could pass the letter to 5672. 5672 opened the letter, photocopied it, and put it back into the envelope and posted it the following day, on 1.11.1967.

Item 8 (List of contents of 51's wallet as on 2.11.1967)

1) Driving licence for Category B vehicles, issued by the Paris Prefect of Police on 20.11.1951
2) Social Security Card No. 1 3103 75 113 078
3) Pass No. 1015, dated 16.10.1967, issued by the Administrative Section of Parthenon
4) Membership Card of Paris University Club with photo of 51 when approx. 20 yrs old
5) 4 First-Class Metro tickets of the R.A.T.P.
6) Partly used book of R.A.T.P. bus tickets
7) Colour photo of two children on a beach:
The beach is very long, no rocks. The hinterland is flat and treeless
The two children (a boy and a girl in bathing costumes) seem roughly the same age, about 8 yrs old – the girl is more robust than the boy. They are both dark. The boy has a squint
8) Colour photo of a woman on horseback
The woman, dark and smiling, seems about 25 yrs old. She is in riding kit: hard cap, short-sleeved shirt, breeches and boots. There is an Arab-looking man in the background
9) Photo of a man (head and shoulders)
The man, aged about 60, is bald but has a thick grey moustache
The photo seems old

46

10) Photo of a woman (head and shoulders)
    The woman is a brunette
    two holes have been pierced to replace the eyes
    the photo is of poor quality; it has been torn in two and
    stuck together. It has also been folded and crumpled, which
    makes it impossible to describe more exactly
11) Photo of five young men in shorts, stripped to the waist,
    with 51 holding a ball
12) Five visiting-cards with the name of Monsieur and Madame
    Dominique Auphal, 31 Avenue de l'Observatoire, Paris VI,
    Odéon 4849
13) Two torn tickets each bearing the word Marignan and a
    number beginning with 154
14) A short broken gold chain
15) A bill dated 14.9.1967 for 658 francs (one jacket, one pair of
    trousers) from the firm 'Arny's'. Written on the bill is the
    word 'done', ringed with a circle
16) A letter dated 6.7.1967 from Flers, signed Jean-François. He
    uses the familiar form of address, talks about old times in the
    regiment and tells 51 that he will be coming to Paris
17) An undated letter from 52 to 51 (signed Liliane, 52's first
    name), 52 is apologizing after a quarrel
18) Three 30-centime postage-stamps
19) A visiting-card with the name M. and Mme Jean Roldoire,
    12 Boulevard des Sablons, 92, Neuilly-sur-Seine, 722 18-44
20) A prescription (illegible) from Dr H. Allix, 54, Rue du Bac,
    Paris VI
21) A postcard reproduction of a painting by Labisse called
    'Mythomécanique'. The card has been cut down in order to
    fit into the wallet. There is no writing on the back
22) Receipt for a registered parcel dated 13.10.1967, 1715 hrs.
    Recipient: Madame Lieuvert, 8 Rue Delambre, Paris XIV
23) A pressed flower (a cornflower?)
24) A card of visiting-card size, with a vertical line down the
    middle. On the left: S. Môme, Antiques, 132 Rue Bonaparte,
    Paris VI, tel. ODE 24 39. On the right: the word 'noted' (in
    print) and the following words, written by hand: 'Despatch
    one refectory table belonging to Monsieur de Maupertain,
    Maupertain Manor (Manche)'. Underneath is printed:

R. C. Seine 59 A 26002

25) A newspaper cutting announcing 51's appointment to the Parthenon

Source and remarks:

On the morning of 2.11.1967, 5353 noted that 51 had changed his suit, leaving his wallet in the inside breast-pocket of his jacket, thus enabling 5353 to examine the wallet and make the above list of the contents.

51 picked up his wallet at lunch-time without making any comment.

When 5672 (our contact-man with 5353) expressed surprise that 5353's list contained no mention of money, 5353 explained that 51 kept his banknotes in a gold or rolled-gold clip.

We have communicated our congratulations to 5353 and made her a special bonus payment for this job which is the best she has accomplished in the last five years.

Item 9 (Memo on 51's behaviour in Rabat over the Ben Barka affair)

51 was a member of the French diplomatic corps in Rabat at the time when the Ben Barka affair brought about so marked a deterioration in Franco-Moroccan relations.

At the first repercussions, 51 adopted an aggressive attitude towards the Moroccan authorities, whom he considered to be beyond any question responsible. He is said to have expressed the most outspoken criticism of the members of the Government and even of the King. Whereas the Embassy, in accordance with its traditional policy, was endeavouring not to envenom our relations with the Moroccan government, and to leave the door open for a later *détente*, 51 abruptly broke off all his personal contacts with the many Moroccans of his acquaintance whilst adopting a cold, indeed almost a hostile attitude in the professional contacts which his official duties required of him.

51's virulence became such that when the French Ambassador was recalled to Paris for consultation, he preferred to take 51 with him in case he might cause an incident during his absence.

It must be noted that such an attitude by 51 was strongly disapproved of by his colleagues at the Embassy, who were most anxious to maintain the traditionally cautious attitude which is the hallmark of French diplomacy. It must also be noted that 51's behaviour was not appreciated at the Quai d'Orsay which was hoping to offset its own fulminations by the relative mildness of its diplomatic representatives in Rabat.

Since 51 had already given ample proof of his ability and intelligence it was impossible to imagine that he had failed to realize the dangers that such an extreme attitude offered for his future career. It would therefore seem likely that the violence of his reaction can be explained only by the force of his sincerity and that he in fact felt personally insulted by what he considered a grave affront to France. On several occasions in the presence of his Embassy colleagues, he used such expressions as: 'Of course I realize that gun-boat diplomacy is dead but they ought to realize that the Fourth Republic is dead, too.'

It seems moreover that 51 accepted his recall to Paris without any resentment, thus confirming the sincerity of his attitude: since he considered that he had acted with complete propriety in this matter, he felt no regrets at the consequences of his actions. 51's complete indifference to this rebuke can also be explained by the fact that he knew that he would find friends in government circles in Paris who would lend a sympathetic ear to his remarks on the dignity of the State and the respect owing to France.

Source: 8274

Item 10 (Memorandum relating to item 11)

Item 11 is a photograph of 51 on the springboard of the Hilton Hotel swimming-pool in Rabat.

It was published on 18.6.1964 by the daily paper *La Vigie Marocaine*, together with a number of other photos, as part of a report on a reception offered by the Hilton Hotel to celebrate the inauguration of Air France's new flight 512. It was an informal garden-party to which children were invited.

Attached: one photograph (item 11)

Item 12 (Memorandum relating to item 13)

Item 13 is a photograph of 52 on horseback clearing a jump.

It was published on 3.9.1965 by the daily paper *La Vigie Marocaine*. It formed part of a newspaper report on the annual horse-show organized by the Rabat Riding Club. 52 was competing on *Nausica* and was placed sixth.

Attached: one photograph (item 13)

Item 14 (Memorandum relating to items 15 to 19)

Items 15: 51 leaving his villa in Delphi on 20.10.1967 at 0845
hrs (5420)

16: 52 leaving 31 Avenue de l'Observatoire on 25.10.1967
at 11.48 hrs (8317)

17: Philippe Lescarre, leaving 29C Rue de l'Université on
31.10.1967 at 0912 hrs (8317)

18: 53, 54 and Marie Marguerite in the Observatoire
Gardens on 26.10.1967 at 1210 hrs (8317)

19: Geneviève de Maupertain, sister of 52, leaving 4 Rue
Duret on 29.10.1967 (8317)

Attached: 5 photographs (items 15 to 19)

Date: 10.11.1967
From: Minerva
To: Apollo
Subject: Labisse

Classification: TS
Ref. no. 2004 NP

Please supply urgently a reproduction of Labisse's picture *Mythomécanique*.

Date: 10.11.1967   Classification: TS
From: Minerva   Ref. no. 2005 GS
To: Mercury
Subject: 52

Objective 52 will be temporarily abandoned.

Date: 10.11.1967
From: Minerva
To: Mars
Subject: 52 and 52A

Classification: TS
Ref. no. 2006 MV

1) Your twin objectives are the man and the woman whose photographs are enclosed

2) The woman is allotted the identification number 52

3) The man is allotted the identification number 52A

4) 52 and 52A meet in the late afternoon in the third-floor flat at 29C Rue de l'Université, Paris VI

5) You will record their conversation

6) 52 may be under a protective screen. The greatest caution will be observed in your execution of the instructions contained in para. 5

7) It must be a solo operation

8) This matter is extremely urgent

Attached: photographs of 52 and 52A

Date: 10.11.1967   Classification: TS
From: Minerva   Ref. no. 2007 VA
To: Mercury
Subject: 51, 53, 55, 56

1) 51: You are to ascertain whether 51 has formed any association with a female since his arrival in Delphi. This matter is particularly urgent since 52 may be joining 51 at any moment.

2) 53: In his letter addressed to 52 under our ref. no. 1994 ZA, 51 refers to a problem arising in connection with 53. You will discover the nature of this problem.

3) 55: 51's and 52's domestic servant is allotted the identification no. 55. We formally instruct 8956 to remain in contact with 55 whilst being careful not to exert excessive pressure on her.

4) 56:

a) 51's secretary at the Parthenon is allotted identification no. 56

b) You will obtain all information possible about 56

c) You will ascertain whether 51 uses the services of 56 in drawing up his confidential reports to the Quai d'Orsay.

Date: 10.11.1967   Classification: TS
From: Apollo   Ref. no. 2008 ZV
To: Minerva
Subject: Labisse

With its customary efficiency, Apollo will arrange to procure for you a reproduction of the work specified, which is not available in our archives. But since Minerva has stressed the urgency of this request, Apollo is happy to oblige Minerva by providing herewith a description of the picture *Mythomécanique*.

The picture is in tones of grey and blue. It represents a naked woman lying on a rocky mountain peak. To the left of this central figure there is a rocky crag, the base of which is surrounded by clouds. On the right, another crag is depicted, on top of which another naked woman with red wings is sitting.

These three subjects fill the bottom half of the canvas. They stand out against a background of blue sky across which three tridents are shown moving from right to left. The speed with which these tridents are moving is indicated by a murky red trail similar to the tail of a comet.

The two women are looking at the tridents.

The woman lying on the central crag is, as we have already said, the main subject of the work. She is lying on her stomach but supported on her right elbow. Her hair is falling over her shoulders as if wet.

Her main feature is her posterior which is disproportionately large compared to the rest of her body. It is not, however, flabby (as we find e.g. in Rubens or Renoir) but on the contrary, elegantly curvaceous and appears to be firm. It is, however, striking in comparison with the slenderness of her waist. This disproportion is emphasized by the woman's posture, with the

58

result that the connoisseur's eye is literally assailed by this exhibition of the posterior, and remains fixed there because the painter has removed any other possible focus of attention (her face is hidden and only her hair can be seen).

The furrow between the buttocks is painted most elaborately.

Should Minerva find this description adequate, we should be grateful to be informed in case the reproduction is no longer needed.

Date: 10.11.1967
From: Minerva
To: Apollo
Subject: Labisse

Classification: TS
Ref. no. 2009 ON

For operational purposes, Apollo's description is adequate.

For non-operational purposes, Minerva's eye is keen to be assailed.

We shall therefore eagerly await the reproduction specified.

Date: 10.11.1967
From: Apollo
To: Minerva
Subject: Labisse

Classification: R
Ref. no. 2010 MN

At the next meeting of Olympus we shall suggest to Jupiter that
your patronymic be changed from Minerva to Lesbos, since this
appears much more in accordance with your real tastes.

Date: 22.11.1967
From: Mercury
To: Minerva
Subject: 56

Classification: TS
Ref. no. 2011 BG

56's duties are identical with those of the secretary whom she is
replacing. They do not give her access to 51's confidential reports
intended for his superiors. 56 takes down 51's correspondence and
types it. She is in charge of the filing system; she takes 51's telephone calls and is responsible for general administrative relations
with other Parthenon departments and for supplying stationery,
etc. These secondary duties, which give her a general idea of 51's
official activity at the Parthenon, do not give her any opportunity
of finding out about his *unofficial* activities which are conducted
by means of direct contacts between 51 and the members of the
various national delegations represented at the Parthenon. For
his confidential reports to the Quai d'Orsay, 51 follows the same
procedure as his predecessor which is, as you will recall, the
following: every Friday at 1500 hrs 51 takes his handwritten
report to the French Embassy and dictates it to one of the two
Chancery secretaries. The typewritten report is then placed in the
diplomatic bag with other items for despatch from the Embassy.
The bag leaves for Paris on the Air France plane taking off at
2230 hrs (Source: 5420).

We would ask you to reconsider whether 56 is still a target of
sufficient interest to justify the instruction contained in para. 4 of
your memo 2007 VA of 10.11.1967: 'You will obtain all possible
information about 56.' Such an investigation when it is remembered that 51 is already under our observation is liable to attract
the attention of rival security services.

Date: 22.11.1967   Classification: TS
From: Minerva   Ref. no. 2012 GG
To: Mercury
Subject: 56

The instruction contained in para. 4(b) of our memo 2007 VA of 10.11.1967 is further defined as follows: 'Ascertain whether 56 has formed any association in Delphi. If so, investigate: a) whether such an association is of a sexual nature, b) whether this association seems likely to exclude other associations.'

As a working hypothesis assume that an extra-professional relationship may arise between 51 and 56.

Date: 22.11.1967   Classification: TS
From : Mars   Ref. no. 2013 IK
To: Minerva
Subject: 52 and 52A

Typescript of a conversation between 52 and 52A recorded on 20.11.67 from 1841 hrs onwards at 29C Rue de l'Université.

52A   ... a bargain/extraordinarily powerful hindquarters/full of spirit and he enjoys it he really does enjoy it/I'm sure you'll take to him

52   I'm just a bit frightened

52A   Don't be stupid/I'm telling you that you've never had anything like it between your legs before/he's young and he's got a lot to learn but by the time I've sorted him out he'll be absolutely O.K./you'll see he'll not give any trouble

52   How old is he

52A   A four-year-old and absolutely O.K./and a wonderful pedigree/he's from querros out of saturn III and tulip/five years ago saturn was carrying off every single prize all over france and navarre

52   I shall miss going riding with you

52A   Not going riding or not being ridden

52   filthy beast
      (laughter from 52A)

52A   that reminds me by the way/I've got a good friend out there/guy de schoelcher/he was still in paris up till three years ago/we went about a lot together for quite a while and did quite a bit of whoring together/if you like I'll give you a letter of recommendation

52   filthy beast

52A   come here
      (12 seconds silence)
52A   Kneel down
      (2 minutes 8 seconds silence)
52A   that's enough
      (40 seconds silence, interrupted after 22 seconds by various
      sounds: clink of glasses, bottle being uncorked, noise of
      liquid being poured out)
52A   and have you decided when you're going to leave
52   he's getting more and more impatient/the day before
      yesterday on the phone he was almost raving mad/I don't
      know what else I can make up/he told me that if I couldn't
      decide he'd come and fetch us himself
52A   how long ago is it since he left in fact
52   A month/exactly a month ago yesterday
52A   he could easily have made a quick trip back/it's not
      difficult by plane/I don't mean for your sake but you
      always told me he was fond of his brats
52   too much work/he's got to familiarize himself with the job/
      it's a very important one you know
52A   says you/I do more work in one day than all those highly
      qualified civil servants in a whole week
52   that's not the point
52A   he puts on false cuffs at the office doesn't he/I can just see
      him wearing his false cuffs and his constipated little arse
      perched on a smelly little cushion
52   he can play tennis better than you
52A   with false cuffs/lift your skirt up/higher than that/I thought
      I told you not to wear knickers
52   that's not true you told me to put on these panties/anyway
      whether I'm wearing them or not doesn't make much
      difference
52A   what are you going to do with all your tart's gear/are you
      going to take it with you
52   that's right/I'll put it on in your memory at official parties
52A   take your clothes off/at once
      (28 seconds silence)
52A   come here
      (32 seconds silence, then an intermittent moaning sound

from 52 for 49 seconds, then 8 seconds silence)

52   what's wrong

52A   nothing/I'm just wondering

52   what are you just wondering

52A   if he really does wear false cuffs/we must find out definitely one way or the other/look take hold of that and ring him up

52   you must be mad

52A   don't stop moving and ring him up/unless you'd prefer me to give you a touch of justine

52   no you're not to do that

52A   don't you like justine anymore

52   I'm afraid of the marks if he were to turn up suddenly without letting me know/last time I had weals all over me

52A   don't stop wriggling blast you/well either you phone him or else you get justine

52   you're revolting

52A   and so is that

    (52 laughs – then the sound of a number being dialled)

52A   that man really put his finger on the problem with his number 22 at Asnières/you're going to get him in two shakes of a lamb's tail/and when I want to warn françoise that I'm on my way so that she can stoke up I'm always told that they can't get through

    (52 laughs)

52A   what are you grinning at/keep moving for christ's sake/ you're not supposed to be going to sleep

52   it takes someone like you to start talking about difficulties in phoning while you're making love

    (52's laughter is becoming hysterical)

52   hello/extension 240/yes 240/look I'm going to hang up/I shan't be able to talk   ..

52A   keep going/and don't forget the false cuffs/or else I'll go and fetch justine – perhaps he's already left the office

52   I doubt it/he works late – in his last letter he/hallo is that you darling (3 seconds) just a little surprise that's all (5 seconds) no nothing at all I felt I wanted to talk to you (6 seconds) yes quite well/they're out with marguerite (18 seconds) of course it's a bore because he'll feel strange (4 seconds) I know that but he'll feel strange in any case

(3 seconds) oh lolo is all right as usual no trouble at all (6 seconds) yes I'll write to you (8 seconds) yes I expect you're fed up with having to wash all those false cuffs of yours (7 seconds) but I know you don't wear them it/was only a joke/you really haven't got any sense of humour at all/what's that (8 seconds) oh leave me alone with the maupertains/(6 seconds) yes splendid at the moment/ absolutely overflowing with energy (3 seconds) yes I think I've got things going nicely now/hallo/I said that/hallo

   (52's voice becomes hoarse, she starts to speak more rapidly and disjointedly)
there's a ring at the door/I'll have to/I think I must/go and see who/I must/I must go/goodbye

   (the sound of the receiver being hung up – 52's moans reach a high pitch in 22 seconds, then silence for 15 seconds)

52   did you enjoy it
52A   not so bad not so bad
52   you'll miss me
52A   you never forget an old bag
52   swine
52A   where shall we go for dinner/pass me the packet I'd like one too
52   garin/say thanks
52A   and how about saturday are you going to be free then/we might go riding at barbizon/I'll let you try him out
52   I prefer to keep roscane/in any case I can't manage saturday we've got his mother to dinner
52A   ashtray/and the saturday after/couldn't you get rid of your kids for one night/we'll spend the night together at barbizon/I'll ask frederick and his wife/I'd be interested to see what you'd be like with frederick
52   I'm scared
52A   you're scared of everything/it's a pity you'll have left before I've been able to finish your training/put on barbara
         (for 12 minutes 8 seconds a record drowns the conversation; doors are heard banging)
52A   couldn't know but I told him that he could have asked me/ are we going/in any case another clanger like that and he's

lost his job/maistre has had his eye on it for months and I've not done anything to discourage him/I think I'll take sauvage/he's not got a lot of experience but he's tremendous on marketing/he had two years at yale/aren't you ready yet/it's queer when I started we almost used false beards to make ourselves look older/I can even remember that I wanted to put on weight to look more responsible and sedate can you imagine it/and the other day salzburger was saying to me/of course at your age there's nothing else you can do now but to stay on with us until you retire/but he's hale and hearty the old bastard/I wonder what the crystal ball foretells/no coronary on the horizon I'm afraid/ what with the rising generation shoving us in the arse and the older generation hanging on like grim death my generation can look forward to a pretty bloody time/oh at last/did you say garin or véfour/oliver was telling me last friday that he's going to launch out into

(ends)

Remarks:

    1) Menelaus who was in charge of the operation did not manage to install a *permanent* device in 52A's flat. 8640 and 8872 called on him under cover of Electricity Board officials. The concierge in charge of the block pointed out that the meters had just been read. 52A's door was opened by a man-servant (probably an Annamite) who remained with them throughout their visit.

    2) The above recording was made in extremely difficult conditions by a long-range receiver. Menelaus points out that there are frequent police patrols in 52A's district and that the radio-van and recording team are liable to attract attention. We request you to inform us if Menelaus is to endeavour to make further recordings.

Date: 27.11.1967
From: Minerva
To: Mercury
Subject: 52A

Classification: TS
Ref. no. 2014 JL

In confirmation of our telephone conversation:

1) You are to ascertain without delay 52A's Barbizon address
2) As soon as this information has been obtained you will leave
   it in the dead letter-box located as follows:
   – Luxembourg Gardens, Paris.
   – Stone urn on the circular balustrade opposite the statue of
   Queen Mary Stuart.

Date: 27.11.1967   Classification: TS
From: Minerva   Ref. no. 2015 OS
To: Mars
Subject: Operation Justine

1) The address at which 52 and 52A will perhaps be spending
    the night of 2/12/1967 – 3/12/1967 will be posted in the dead
    letter box located as follows:
    – Luxembourg Gardens, Paris.
    – Stone urn on the circular balustrade opposite the statue of
    Queen Mary Stuart.
2) On receipt of present instructions, Menelaus will check the
    letter-box every three hours.
3) As soon as he has received the address, he will set up a
    recording device there.
4) Menelaus will investigate the possibility of filming or photo-
    graphing any sexual intercourse between 52 and 52A and
    possibly with another couple of friends, on the night of 2 to
    3/12/1967.
5) Even should the operation indicated in the preceding para.
    seem to present considerable difficulties, we request you, if
    the opportunity presents itself, to take the appropriate action.
6) This operation should not be undertaken if Menelaus detects
    any covering of 52 on the part of a rival security service.
7) Apart from this eventuality, we rely on you to *pounce*.
8) This is to be a solo *repeat* solo operation by Menelaus.
9) It will be given the code-name Justine.

Date: 28.11.1967   Classification: TS
From: Mercury   Ref. no. 2016 GD
To: Minerva
Subject: 53

53 was born on 30.8.1959 in Madrid (Spain).

From his earliest age, his health gave rise to concern to his parents. He is both sickly and highly strung. His height and weight are both below average.

When 51 and 52 went to Rabat, they were worried at the possible effect of the Moroccan climate on him and sent him to stay with 52's parents. He spent thirteen months at Maupertain. This stay proved relatively successful from the physical point of view, since 53 put on height and some weight; but it was disastrous from the psychological point of view. In fact, 52's father took a dislike to his puny grandson who has a squint and suffers from persistent enuresis. He determined to resort to vigorous measures and cure his enuresis by punishment and poking fun at him in the presence of others. He was not prepared to allow 53 to be left-handed. He frequently tied his left arm behind his back to force him to use his right hand.

During his stay at Maupertain, 53 attended the local nursery school where his squint and his bed-wetting made him the permanent butt of the other children. His initial period at the school was most unhappy. He later developed dyslexia, probably as a result of the attempt to counter his left-handedness. Even now, he still inverts the order of his syllables.

51 decided to take 53 away with him during a leave which he spent at Maupertain with 52. This decision precipitated a grave crisis between 51 and 52. 52 was mainly concerned with 53's physical condition and she considered that he was much better since

71

he had been at Maupertain. It may be conjectured that, having been brought up in the country, 52 attached less importance than 51 to the psychological environment and to the factors likely to warp 53's sensibility.

As 52 joined forces with her parents, 51 had to bear the whole brunt of the attack from the Maupertain clan. During some of the discussions, 51 displayed such violence that the servants talked of a possible break-up of the marriage.

Since that time, 51 and 53 have been very close. 52 undoubtedly feels motherly affection for 53 but she seems at a loss to deal with the psychological problems involved. She does not attach the same importance to these problems as 51. 52 feels more in touch with 54, who is an uncomplicated little girl.

We have no information about 53 in Rabat.

In Paris, 53 attends the Steiner School, 78 Rue d'Assas, VI. It is a private school run by Mademoiselle Valérie Steiner, who holds a higher degree and is Montessori trained. She specializes in dealing with disturbed children.

The 'problem' mentioned by 51 in his letter ref. 1994 ZA to 52 which your memo 2007 VA of 10.11.1967 requested us to elucidate might be that of finding a private school in Delphi comparable to the one that 53 is attending in Paris.

This supposition is lent weight by a sentence in 51's letter ref. 1998 JP to 53: 'I'm busy looking for a school for you here which will be as nice as Madame Valérie's.'

Source: Composite report based on information collected by 8956 (55) and 8218

Date: 5.12.1967   Classification: TS
From: Mars   Ref. no. 2017 JV
To: Minerva
Subject: Operation Justine

Confirming our telephone conversation, Menelaus reports by
W/T that Operation Justine has given positive results.

Date: 11.12.1967
From: Mercury
To: Minerva
Subject: 51

Classification: TS
Ref. no. 2018 VV

The reply to your question in para. 1 of your memo 2007 VA of 10/11/1967 is negative up to and including 25/11/1967. 51 has been kept under strict observation but no trace of any feminine association has been discovered.

51 leaves home at about 0830 hrs to proceed to the Parthenon in the official car with chauffeur made available by the French Embassy. He returns at about 1300 hrs. He eats the light lunch prepared by 5353 except when he has a working luncheon, which is frequently the case. He leaves at about 1345-1400 hrs. He remains at the office until 1930 hrs or even 2000 hrs. He dines in a little restaurant close to the Parthenon when he has no official dinner or is not invited out to dinner which is frequently the case. Hitherto all such invitations have come from members of foreign delegations.

Observation is continuing.

Date: 11.12.1967   Classification: TS
From: Mercury   Ref. no. 2019 DM
To: Minerva
Subject: 51

On 22.11.1967, 51 informed 5353 that she could take the following day off.

On 24.11.1967, 5353 found cigarette ends (Gitanes and Gauloises) in the ash-trays in the house: 51 is a non-smoker.

Whilst doing the housework, 5353 noticed that the furniture had been shifted. Care had been taken to replace it in its former position but dust had been removed in such a way that 5353 had no doubt as to what had been done.

5353 points out that it will be difficult to intercept a letter from 52 to 51. 51 receives his mail before going to the office and takes it with him.

5353 informs us that on the morning of 24.11.1967, 51 left for the office carrying files, which is something he had not previously done.

Remarks:
1) 5353 receiving a day off, the presence of a large number of cigarette ends and the moving of the furniture might indicate that French security services had combed the villa to ascertain if it was bugged.
2) As far as we know, no check of this sort had been undertaken since 15/12/1958.

Date: 11.12.1967   Classification: TS
From: Mercury   Ref. no. 2020 VA
To: Minerva
Subject: 56

The investigation of 56 is proceeding. A composite report will be submitted shortly.

As a preliminary indication enclosed please find a letter sent by 56 on 4.12.1967 to Mademoiselle Elisabeth Vaneste of 8 Rue Budé, Paris IV.

This letter was intercepted in the following circumstances:

On 17.11.1967 at about 0800 hrs, 5404, whose task is to keep 56 under observation, saw the latter leave her block of flats carrying an envelope. 56 opened the envelope and took out the letter contained therein. She then crumpled the envelope up into a ball and threw it onto the pavement as she started to read the letter.

5404 picked up the envelope, on the back of which was written the name and address of the sender: Elisabeth Vaneste, 8 Rue Budé, Paris IV.

We instructed 8972 to gather information on Elisabeth Vaneste. On 7.12.1967 at 0900 hrs, 8972 went to 8 Rue Budé, to make a reconnaissance. The block has no porter. Each tenant's mail is placed in a letter-box under his or her name. In Elisabeth Vaneste's letter-box there were three envelopes which 8972 managed to extract. Two of them contained advertising material, the third contained 56's letter. After being photocopied, the letter was replaced in the envelope and put back into the box.

Enclosure: 56's letter

My dear Liza,

What a worrier you are! Is it because you're getting more like Don Quixote every day or because I'm becoming more like Sancho Panza? So you must stop tormenting yourself and put your trust in the Lord who can see all your weaknesses and forgive them. And Christmas is coming. How I love Christmas! Advent which leads up to it tells us so much about this holy mystery and we must never cease to marvel at it, don't you agree? In some operettas or religious plays in the Midi there's one character who appeals to me more than any other: it's the one who MARVELS. Perhaps he is rather silly (or, at least, guileless) but his admiration is so *genuine* and so *simple*. Don't imagine I'm becoming 'sanctimonious' (and that word in itself has a rather disagreeable flavour, too) but you must admit that there *is* something to be admired in such an attitude. Don't you agree?

Anyway, all the things that I hear about in this place are enough to prevent me from becoming smug, I promise you. The day before yesterday, the sub-committee of the C.A.S.A.R. showed a film on famine in India in the afternoon. The big lecture-theatre was packed and you could have heard a pin drop. What dreadful poverty! You felt ashamed at eating at lunch-time and realizing that you'd be having another meal in the evening. Solange Pescaud who was sitting beside me couldn't help crying. I came back to the office terribly moved. I met my boss in the corridor. He'd just been watching the show, too. I told him how glad I was to be working in an organization that was trying to find a cure for such frightful things, but he replied in his usual frigid way with that little smile I've told you about: 'My dear Miss Mouriac, since Nehru took over our companies there, India no longer belongs to our sphere of influence. The salvation of the Indians probably lies in being taken over by the Chinese with all the economic reforms that would follow, but as that is not likely to happen overnight, they'll go on kicking the bucket for some time yet with their mouths wide open, and their toes stuck out, if you don't object to the expression.' He's always using phrases like that that make your blood run cold. Well, my dear, I was still so upset that I plucked up courage to ask him: 'But what about the children, Monsieur Auphal? Didn't you see all those poor little children with their tummies all swollen up?' Do you, know, Liza, I felt almost scared that I'd hurt him. His self-assured look changed so that he looked quite young and defenceless and he muttered: 'Ah yes, the children, of course there are the children.' And then he added in a very harsh voice: 'When children are miserable, it's God's way of spitting in the face of mankind.' Such a blasphemous remark! It horrified me and then, in the evening, my mind went back to that splendid lecture by Father Dupond in the Boulevard Montparnasse, do you remember: 'Insulting God means recognizing him.' I wish you could have seen his expression when he said that to me. He must certainly be a man who has suffered a great deal. Anyway, he's a very pleasant man to work for and he keeps his distance. I believe he's doing a great deal, particularly with the African delegates.

Liza, I can't help thinking all the time about the famine in India and I think that there's not really very much we can do to improve things in our humble position in life. Only God can govern everything and see that everything is for the best. That's why prayer is the best remedy: I find it very comforting to have such a wonderful thing to be able to do, don't you?

Just one more thing before I stop all this chat: I received an extraordinarily nice letter from Mother Dominique, I really was delighted! She asked after you and wrote: 'How I should like to meet her again.' Take note! She's the prioress at Rouen House (Rue Verte). Meanwhile, she asked to be remembered to you.

Liza, I must stop now. Let me send you as a pre-Christmas greeting every good wish for peace and joy and goodwill on

earth as well as my kindest regards from your most affectionate
Sylvia.

P.S. You didn't even tell me what's become of dear Ruth Hemel.
Stuck-up as usual? (I mean her, not you!) Give her a hug from
me and Jeannine as well.

Date: 11.12.1967
From: Minerva
To: Mercury
Subject: 56

Classification: T S
Ref. no. 2022 UN

Objective 56 will be abandoned forthwith.

You are to request Clio for 5353's dossier and Mercury for the latest information concerning her.

5353 is a paid agent who for a number of years has supplied us with little information, and that relatively unimportant. Her performance at the moment has suddenly improved, both in quantity and quality. An investigation is thus required into her position. You are therefore urgently to initiate screening procedure 3.

Date: 18.12.1967   Classification: TS
From: Mars   Ref. no. 2024 VI
To: Minerva
Subject: Operation Justine

After examination of the material forwarded to us, it would appear that the above-mentioned operation, contrary to the expectations expressed in Menelaus W/T report, has not been a complete success.

The listening and recording equipment installed by the Menelaus section has proved defective. The tape, although winding normally, failed to record. The reason for this is unknown. The defective instrument will be forwarded to Vulcan for a thorough examination and report.

The Menelaus section succeeded in photographing sexual intercourse between 52 and 52A. Attached please find 12 photos numbered 1 to 12. The faces of the couple are invisible on photos 8, 9, 10 and 11 as a result of the posture adopted but 52 is identifiable by a brown mark on the lower left buttock. (This mark can be seen on photos 4 and 7, where 52's face is partially visible.)

Attached: 12 photos numbered 1 to 12

Date: 18.12.1967   Classification: TS
From: Minerva   Ref. no. 2025 OJ
To: Mars
Subject: Operation Justine

The failure of the tape to record is unimportant. The purpose of the operation was more visual than aural and the photos are superb.

Please forward our congratulations to Menelaus.

Date: 20.12.1967   Classification: TS
From: Mercury   Ref. no. 2026 LV
To: Minerva
Subject: 52A

It may interest you to know that, according to a report from
8016, on Monday 4.12.1967 at 0910 hours, the police called at
52A's house at Barbizon.

Date: 20.12.1967   Classification: TS
From: Minerva   Ref. no. 2027 OM
To: Mars
Subject: Operation Justine

1) Para. 8 of our memo 2015 OS of 27.11.1967 ordered that the above should be a solo operation.

2) You will ask Menelaus if he acted in accordance with this order or whether, on the contrary, he was in contact with any members of the Mercury staff. This request is to be treated as a matter of *extreme urgency*.

3) You will stress with Menelaus the gravity of this matter and insist on a frank and complete answer. You will inform him that we shall be prepared to overlook any disregard of instructions that may have taken place with regard to para. 8 of our memo of 27.11.1967 but that our joint interests require us to be fully informed on this matter.

4) You are to report forthwith.

Date: 21.12.1967   Classification: TS
From: Mercury   Ref. no. 2028 UA
To: Minerva
Subject: 51

5672 has interrogated 5353 concerning the files that 51 took away with him on the morning of 24.11.1967.

5353 stated that on arriving at the villa she discovered that 51 was still in bed, whereas he would normally be having his breakfast. She started her cleaning in 51's office. She noticed that the writing table was covered with open files. On the writing-pad there was a file of hand-written documents. 51 came downstairs a few minutes later. He told 5353 that he had worked very late that night, and that he thought he had earned 'a bit of a lie-in'. He left the house taking the files and memoranda with him.

5672 asked 5353 why she hadn't reported these details at the time of their last conversation (5353 had on that occasion merely reported that 51 had left for the office on 24.11.1967 carrying some files – cf. our memo 2019 DM of 11.12.1967). 5353 replied that what had particularly struck her was the presence of cigarette ends and the shifting of the furniture.

The interest of this information lies in the fact that the 24.11.1967 was a Friday. It may be surmised therefore that 51 had brought home on Thursday evening the files needed for the preparation of his weekly report (which he hands in every Friday at the French Embassy to be placed in the diplomatic bag) and that he wrote out this report during the night of Thursday to Friday.

It is not impossible that this may happen again on a future occasion.

We further inform you that the room used by 51 as his office is on the ground floor. His bedroom is on the first floor, at the other end of the building.

Date: 25.12.1967   Classification: TS
From: Mars   Ref. no. 2029 WM
To: Minerva
Subject: Operation Justine

We herewith confirm our verbal report: Menelaus' reply to the question contained in your memo 2027 OM of 20.12.1967 is negative.

We venture to add that if Menelaus has on occasion exceeded his instructions or shown himself temperamental, he has never failed to prove himself completely reliable whenever the gravity of the circumstances required it.

We reiterate our complete readiness to provide you with *maximum* co-operation at all times.

Date: 26.12.1967   Classification: TS
From: Minerva   Ref. no. 2030 DP
To: Jupiter
Subject: 51

We send you herewith for your perusal and assessment copies of all the documents relating to the dossier of 51.

Since 11.9.67, the date on which Minerva was informed of 51's appointment to the Parthenon, we have endeavoured to gather the fullest possible information on the objective with the aim of discovering some method of attack.

Despite some reluctance on the part of Mercury in carrying out instructions, the material that we have succeeded in collecting has indicated that 51's weak point might be 52, by reason of 52's association with 52A.

On 27.11.1967, we ordered Mars to carry out operation Justine. Since no collaboration by Mercury was required for this operation, we instructed Mars to act alone. It is for this reason that we informed Mercury in our memo 2005 GS of 10.11.1967 that objective 52 was to be temporarily abandoned as far as they were concerned. No supplementary order relating to 52A was required since Mercury had received no instructions in relation to investigating 52A or placing him under observation.

Mercury's memo 2026 LV of 20.12.1967 proves that, in complete disregard of our instructions, Mercury has continued to show interest in 52 and, secondarily, in 52A. Mercury, in the memo under ref., has clearly felt impelled to inform us of a police visit to 52A's house in the country. Incidentally, we would emphasize that such a visit could only be a coincidence, since Menelaus made no mention of any incident connected with Operation Justine liable to give rise to any intervention on the

89

part of the French police. It is plain that Mercury can only have become aware of such a visit if it had placed 52A's house at Barbizon under observation, something which it has not only never been asked to do but which was, in fact, expressly forbidden by the terms of our memo 2005 GS of 10.11.1967.

It is unlikely that Mercury would have decided to embark on a surveillance operation of this sort by chance. It is more likely that after having placed 52A's address in the dead letter-box in the Luxembourg Gardens, Mercury stationed an agent nearby to keep watch on Menelaus' agent when he came to collect the address. Being thus informed that we were initiating an operation against 52 and 52A, Mercury undertook, *on its own initiative*, to place 52A's Barbizon house under observation.

In the first place, therefore, we wish to protest against Mercury's marked tendency, of which this incident is yet another example, to exceed its terms of reference, which are purely executive.

In the second place, we feel bound to draw your attention to the grave nature of the above facts. By employing its own agents to keep watch on those of Mars, Mercury was guilty of *actively infringing* the strict rule of inter-departmental independence and secrecy and the security principles which it appears so anxious to invoke on paper. Such conduct has the effect of encouraging a sectarian attitude in our agents which can only prejudice the unity and efficiency of the service.

We therefore request you to be so good as to instruct Hecate to undertake the following mission: 1) to verify whether internal regulations have been infringed in the above-mentioned circumstances; 2) if so, to submit to you proposals for a reorganization which will guarantee that no operation by any section of the service will be impeded or jeopardized by irresponsible behaviour on the part of Mercury.

Copy for information to Mercury

Date: 28.12.1967
From: Mercury
To: Jupiter
Subject: 51

Classification: TS
Ref. no. 2031 RV

The facts are simple.

Following the request made by Minerva in its memo 2014 JL of 27.11.1967, we instructed 8025 to ascertain 52A's address at Barbizon. 8025 accomplished this mission. 8016 placed the address in the dead letter-box indicated by Minerva. We did not station any agent near this letter-box nor did we, on our own initiative, place 52A's house in Barbizon under observation.

On 3.12.1967 at 1900 hrs 8025 reported the following facts to his head of section Socrates. On that day, at about 1300 hrs, 8025 had taken his children for a walk in the forest of Fontaine-bleau (we draw your attention to the fact that the 3rd was a Sunday). On arrival at Barbizon, 8025 forbade his children to go playing amongst the rocks for fear of an accident. He took them with him into the woods to the left of the road leading from Barbizon to Fontainebleau. They had gone only a few hundred yards when their attention was drawn to a group of six or eight people standing round a hole approximately 16 inches deep. At the bottom of this hole lay the dead body of a dog which, according to 8025, was of the breed known as Alsatian. A man explained to 8025 that his own dog, an Irish setter, had started digging a hole at this spot and had uncovered the dog's body. Most of those present were of the opinion that the body should be left where it was and the hole covered in, since it seemed to them that it was merely a dog which had died and been buried by its master. A woman noticed, however, that the top of the dog's skull bore the marks of a deep wound, thus suggesting that it had been killed by

91

means of a blunt instrument. The owner of the Irish setter expressed the view that either the Society for the Prevention of Cruelty to Animals or the police should be informed. The woman undertook to do this. 8025 went on with his children and as they had been upset by what they had seen, he took them for a cup of chocolate in a Barbizon café. He mentioned the discovery of the dog's body to the waitress, who asked him where it had been found. He described the spot. The waitress then put forward the suggestion that the dog might have been taken into the woods by a Parisian wanting to get rid of the animal or else that it might have come from one of the houses in the Rue Gabriel-Séailles, which was only two or three hundred yards from the spot mentioned by 8025. On hearing the name of the street, which he knew was the one in which 52A owned a house, 8025 wondered whether the death of the dog might not be in some way related to a current operation. On his return to Paris, he informed Socrates of this possibility.

Since Socrates had no time to report back, he took the initiative of detailing 8016 to proceed to Barbizon the following morning with instructions to keep watch on 52A's house and to investigate whether the discovery of the dead dog had had any repercussions. 8016 was able to observe the arrival of two policemen at 0910 hrs. They remained in 52A's house till 1048 hrs. 52A opened the door himself. 8016 considered that this visit was possibly connected with the discovery of the dead dog but he refrained from asking any questions in the village for fear of attracting the attention of the police.

Such are the facts leading to our memo 2026 LV of 20.12.1967 to Minerva.

We are of the opinion that our men's behaviour has been in full accordance with what is to be expected from active and alert agents. 8025 *had* to report to Socrates. Socrates, considering rightly or wrongly that the incident might be connected with an objective – 52A – on which his team had been working only one week previously, *had* to take the initiative of detailing 8016 to Barbizon. Minerva, logically, *ought* to be grateful to us for having notified 52A's contact with members of the police force, even if it turned out to be only the result of such an ordinary event as the death of a watch-dog.

We are not aware here at Mercury of the latest developments initiated by Minerva in relation to 52 and 52A. We are too familiar with Minerva's methods to imagine that it could have been guilty of mistakes likely to disclose to any rival security service its interest in 52A and, as a logical consequence, in 52 and 51.

We are the more convinced of this inasmuch as our most recent reports have been stressing the excellent chances of success that have been opened up by 5353, through our contact man 5672 in Delphi. Such possibilities lead us to envisage a far more direct and less problematical hold on 51 than any that we might achieve through 52. Since we refuse to believe that Minerva can have jeopardized such hopes by ill-considered action against 52 and 52A, we fail to understand its attitude towards us.

Will you please inform us whether we are to congratulate Socrates and 8025 for their initiative or whether on the contrary we are to take disciplinary action against them and, if so, what.

Copy for information to Minerva

Date: 28.12.1967　　　　　Classification: TS
From: Minerva　　　　　　Ref. no. 2032 JB
To: Mars
Subject: Operation Justine

Request information from Menelaus whether above-mentioned operation involved liquidation of Alsatian dog and, if so, in what circumstances.

Treat as a matter of extreme urgency.

Date: 29.12.1967   Classification: TS
From: Mars   Ref. no. 2033 AZ
To: Minerva
Subject: Operation Justine

Menelaus' reply is in the affirmative.
52A's property at Barbizon was guarded by a watch-dog.
Menelaus' plan involved its temporary neutralization by an
application of Lethe. The agent in charge of the equipment was
delayed by the breakdown of his car and it proved impossible
to keep to the prearranged plan. Menelaus proceeded to liquidate
the dog, with adequate security precautions, in such a way as to
lead 52A to assume that his dog had run away.

Date: 30.12.1967   Classification: TS
From: Jupiter   Ref. no. J 4813
To: Minerva
Subject: 51

Following your verbal explanation, I have taken the following
decisions:

1) I intend to put a stop once and for all to this internal
dissension in which you have given such blatant proof of spite
and ill-will. Mercury's memo 2031 RV of 28.12.1967 gives a
perfectly adequate explanation of the activities of its agents.
Contrary to your assertion, Mercury can in no way be blamed
for not informing you until 20.12.1967 of the visit by the two
members of the police to 52A's house, since Mercury could not
have known that Menelaus had carried out his operation at 52A's
so clumsily that the police visit was a matter of some gravity.
8016's report did not in itself justify any communication of this
information being made as a matter of urgency.

2) The consequences of Menelaus' clumsiness are more serious
than you purport to believe.

The theories that you have been endeavouring to uphold seem
to me extremely fanciful and unworthy of your critical acumen.
It is impossible to expect the police and 52A to attribute the
liquidation of the dog to the action of thieves preparing to
commit a burglary. Burglars would have liquidated the dog on
the night of their attempt and would certainly never have aroused
52A's suspicions by eliminating it several days beforehand. 52A
and the police will thus have looked round for a more rational
explanation of the disappearance of the dog. It is to be feared
that they may have found it in the association between 52A and
52. With regard to this point, your belief that 52A is the sort of

man who, while thrashing his mistresses, would be loth to disclose their identity to third parties, seems to us to reveal a peculiarly inept psychological understanding. In any case, the extent and accuracy of the information possessed by the French police as to the private lives of their compatriots have been brought home to us so frequently that we dare not hope that they will have continued to remain in ignorance for long of 52's visits to 52A. Finally, the fact that the two policemen should have remained in 52A's house from 0910 till 1048 hrs suggests that they carried out a close examination of the premises which may have led them to discover traces of Operation Justine. Any discovery of this nature would have immediately made them warn the French security authorities.

3) In view of this eventuality, all current or projected operations directly or indirectly affecting 51 are forthwith suspended until further orders.

4) Agent 5353, whom Mercury is handling with great skill and caution, is specifically excluded from this order, with the proviso that any extension of this agent's activities shall be dependent on successful completion of the screening operation currently being undertaken by Hecate.

5) Whilst awaiting the outcome of this operation, Mercury will continue to keep 51 under *slight* observation in order to discover whether any rival security service has been put on its guard by Menelaus' clumsiness and placed 51 under protective cover.

6) If such is the case, Mercury will immediately break off contact with 5353 and report back.

7) Menelaus is to be reprimanded and this reprimand is to be entered in his personal file.

8) Should the assumption made in para. 5 prove exact, thus entailing the ultimate failure of the operation we are conducting against 51, more vigorous disciplinary action will be taken against all concerned, without distinction of rank or seniority.

Date: 30.12.1967   Classification: TS
From: Minerva   Ref. no. 2034 RA
To: Mercury
Subject: 51

Herewith four paras. concerning your organization extracted
from memo J 4813 of today's date addressed to us from Jupiter:

3) I hereby order that all current or projected actions directly
or indirectly affecting 51 be suspended until further orders.

4) Agent 5353 is specifically excluded from this order, with the
proviso that any extension of this agent's activities shall be
dependent on successful completion of the screening operation
currently being undertaken by Hecate.

5) Whilst awaiting the outcome of this process, Mercury will
continue to keep 51 under *slight* observation in order to discover
whether any rival security service has placed 51 under protective
cover.

6) If such is the case, Mercury will immediately break off
contact with 5353 and report back.

The instructions contained in your directive J 4813 of today's date are being implemented.

We wish to give you our assurance that it has never been our purpose to adopt a hostile attitude towards any section of the service. Minerva is well aware of the disastrous results that might ensure from such conduct. If any words which we have used, whether verbally or in our written memoranda, have seemed to imply animus directed against Mercury, then it is our inadequate expression which must be blamed since, on the contrary, we are generally well pleased with Mercury's activities, especially with the skilful way in which it is handling 5353. A favourable result of the screening operation now being conducted by Hecate would open up interesting possibilities.

Whilst deploring the clumsiness shown by Menelaus during Operation Justine, we venture to point out that this operation has put us in possession of material of undoubted interest. The tape recorded in 52A's Paris rooms and the photographs taken in his Barbizon house, do, in our view, offer a possibility of exerting indirect pressure on 51.

We seek your authority to forward the relevant items of 51's file to Aesculapius with the request to analyse them and to investigate whether the information available on 52 seems to them suitable to make 52 exploitable.

We would stress that such an examination in no way runs counter to the instructions contained in your directive of today's date. Should Aesculapius' diagnosis be favourable, there would be no question of taking any action before ensuring ourselves that Menelaus' clumsiness has not had any unfortunate consequences.

Should these two conditions (a favourable diagnosis from Aesculapius and absence of any counter-action by other security forces) be fulfilled, the conclusion might be drawn, in our view, that the subject is vulnerable and the first phase of the operation could be considered successful.

Date: 31.12.1967   Classification: TS
From: Jupiter   Ref. no. J 7215
To: Minerva
Subject: 51

Authorization hereby granted to forward the relevant items in 51's file to Aesculapius.

Date: 3.1.1968
From: Minerva
To: Aesculapius
Subject: 51

Classification: TS
Ref. no. 2036 BA

– Herewith the relevant documents from the file of 51, with the following reference numbers:

1977 LQ	1994 ZA	2011 BG
1979 AV	1995 OV	2018 VV
1980 UC	1996 MO	2020 VA
1981 GG	1997 PT	2021 JO
1982 CN	1998 JP	2012 GG
1983 UG	1999 HN	2013 IK
1984 KV	2000 TG	2016 GD
1985 FF	2001 UR	
1986 MD	(+ 1 photo)	2007 VA
1986 Md	2002 VP	2008 ZV
1990 GP	(+ 1 photo)	2024 VI
1992 ZQ	2003 VA	(+ 12 photos)
1993 TR	(+ 5 photos)	

– List of the principal persons involved:
- 51: the objective
- 52: 51's wife
- 52A: 52's lover
- 53: 51's and 52's son
- 54: 51's and 52's daughter

55:   51's and 52's maidservant
56:   51's secretary

Since 51's morals and way of life seem likely to exclude any direct exploitation, we have focused our particular attention on 52, whose association with 52A presents considerable interest, as will be seen from the attached material.

Our working hypothesis is that 51's only real interests are in his work. His emotional life is polarized round his children, especially round 53. His sexual activity seems somewhat below average. All our information concerning him suggests that he is interested only in his career.

This career is a promising one, thanks to 51's intrinsic qualities and to the friends he has in French governmental circles, but it is a career centred on the French diplomatic service in which, traditionally, great importance is still attached to the way of life of its members and their acceptance of certain strict conventions.

Should the photographs and recordings relating to 52 and 52A come to the knowledge of 51's colleagues, his diplomatic career would be brought to an abrupt end. Even if no official disciplinary action were to be taken against him, the resultant scandal would be such that he would have no other choice than to resign.

We believe that the threat of thus informing 51's colleagues would be sufficient to soften up 51 and make him exploitable.

We ask for your confirmation of this hypothesis.

The investigation of 51 has been a matter of some delicacy and continues to cause us considerable concern. We therefore make a most earnest appeal to Aesculapius' good will in this matter in the hope that they will devote particular care and attention to this dossier and leave no stone unturned to produce a positive diagnosis.

Attached: 33 documents and 19 photographs

Date: 5.1.1968　　　　　　　　　Classification: TS
From: Mercury　　　　　　　　　Ref. no. 2037 VO
To: Minerva
Subject: 51

Enclosed herewith:
1) letter from 52 to 51 of 14.12.1967 intercepted and copied by
   5353
2) letter from the French Radio and Television Office of
   9.10.1967 (date of postmark) addressed to 51, intercepted
   and copied by 5353

Two enclosures

Darling,

You've been quite beastly and you know it. It's true that Hervé *was* my responsibility and not yours but I did warn you straightaway as soon as the question of money came up. If we'd had a receipt we should have been all right but of course it wouldn't suit your *persona* to ask for a receipt! 'Of course not, I wouldn't dream of it between friends' you say waving your hands about with a smile – in public and then you take it out on me on the phone like a peasant when we can't see how we can get our money back. It's really not fair and you know it. You can't say Simone didn't warn you. She phoned me yesterday to say that it served you right and that Hervé would be a fool not to go on acting like that as long as he could find fatheads like us. You can imagine how charming it was for me to be called a fat-head by such a disagreeable woman as Simone. I was tempted to reply that I'd sooner have a fat head than a great big fat bottom like her. And not very fragrant at that.

The Durands gave their annual bunfight two days ago. I went with Ginette and Michel. Michel's rather under the weather at the moment. Snowed under with work etc. Lots of lawyers-cum-spouses, all busily pursuing briefs as madly as their husbands, a lot of up-and-coming young civil servants trying to behave like grand senior secretaries in the Treasury whilst continuing to dress like commercial travellers. And, of course, hardly any smoked salmon, and no caviar at all. I forgot to mention our family scribbler, your brother, who walked round the room with his

105

usual conceited silly grin on his face dropping hints that he had an absolutely mar-vell-ous magnum opus on the stocks. The children were all there of course (just like the Durands that) and the assembled company kept finding it *so* sweet as the little horrors kept knocking glasses of champagne over – which was nothing more than it deserved, by the way. And also by the way, Thérèse has had her baby – *two* months early. Absolutely delighted as you might expect to be different from other people. I went to see her in hospital and was regaled by a long harangue on the genius (*sic*) of premature babies. It seems that Caesar, Churchill and God knows who else were all two months premature. She thought this was a stroke of genius (sic again). It was *madly amusing* that *she'd* done it too. We talked about horses for a while and I couldn't help laughing to myself when she told me about her powers in the saddle as if she was a sort of Janou Lefèvre (I think she'd be better on a bidet).

My wagging tongue is beginning to dry up, but since we can't be beastly together at the moment, we shall each have to be beastly separately. Your portrait of His Excellency N'Diombe literally convulsed me with laughter. It's extraordinary how amusing you can be when you're being unkind. But keep it for other people, darling, and don't take your miserable investments out on me. That's not asking a lot, is it?

The scarlatina is taking its course. His temperature is down but he's tired out and spends the whole of the day in bed. And of course it's not like him to try and make an effort to get well. He seems perfectly happy. He's still as enthusiastic as ever about the stars, in fact more so. I spend my days ferreting round bookshops looking for books on astronomy that aren't too difficult. I must confess that all that business of light-years is absolutely fascinating and one feels so petty and insignificant . . . I can't look at the sky now without asking myself idiotic questions that I haven't thought of since I was fifteen. All the same, I wonder if it's not perhaps the wrong thing for someone as young and sensitive as Steve. But I know that's your pigeon, not mine . . . Anyway, you don't need to worry: I see that he does his reading exercises every morning although Cain doesn't seem to show any desire to follow the straight and narrow. He's really rather sweet with his bandage over his eye. I often tell myself that he looks like a pirate's son although you're the man *least* like a pirate that I know. I was meant to marry a pirate, really. Or rather, a corsair: it's more distinguished. You finished up at the end of a yard-arm anyway but you had the King's commission in your pocket as a consolation.

How sad, that miserable scarlatina keeping us away from you and your black men. But you'll come over for Christmas won't you? Dr Le Noir says the risk of catching it is very slight and I should say it's nil but your dear Mama thinks it's enormous. The poor old dear confessed to me that you hadn't had scarlatina as if this was a weakness that could be blamed on the way she brought you up. All the same, you must be careful not to take it back to your blackamoors who would then die off like flies or Indians catching smallpox. The French representative at O.R.V.A. suspected of genocide would really be hilarious! Lolo is the same as ever. Incidentally, I wonder if the time hasn't come to start calling her just Elodie. One must beware of pet names. They're charming at first and then they cling to you like a leech. You're the first person to laugh at poor old Jacky, with her big bottom and her double chin, who I suppose will go on being called Jacky to the end of her days . . . And talking of Lolo or rather Elodie I found her yesterday evening parading in front of my mirror all dressed up in bath towels like a carnival queen. She at least is not going to be a tomboy! Every night when she goes to bed she religiously kisses your photo after saying her prayers. I think she's very fond of you.

We'll be expecting you next week. I think that Father Christmas has something up his sleeve for you. *Two* Father Christmases, even, because in Lolo's work-basket I found a little gadget that can only be intended for you or a boyfriend. As we needn't expect any danger from that direction yet, I imagine that you will be the happy recipient.

A kiss from your affectionate wife.

P.S. Don't forget the cheque for Delattre. She's already telephoned several times. I'm forwarding an old letter from ORTF which has been left lying about in 'Oublier Palerme' for weeks.

Remarks: The above letter was discovered on 26.12.1967 by 5353 in a jacket left behind by 51 whilst on a visit to Paris. 5353 copied it and put the original back in the jacket pocket.

OFFICE OF THE
FRENCH RADIO
AND TELEVISION
National Licence Centre
9 Avenue Janvier
RENNES (I & V)
Rennes
(date as postmark)

FINAL DEMAND
BEFORE PROSECUTION

Dear Sir/Madam,

I note that, despite our preliminary warning and demand, you have failed to pay the licence fee due more than five months ago.

In view of this and as you have been previously warned, this fee is hereby increased by an amount equivalent to 60% of the original sum.

The amount now owing is shown on the attached slip and you will doubtless appreciate that it is in your own interests to settle this account forthwith.

Should you however fail to take advantage of this final request, we shall find ourselves under the obligation to have recourse to legal proceedings in order to recover, in due form, the amount now owing.

Settlement of this account may be made by any of the methods indicated on the back of this letter, but I draw your attention to the fact that the giro-form attached cancels and replaces that sent you previously.

I am, Sir/Madam,
    Your obedient servant,
        Head of National Licence Centre

Remarks: Letter copied by 5353 on the same date and in the same circumstances as the preceding ref. 2038 MM.

Herewith document 2038 MM to be attached to file 51.

One enclosure

Date: 6.1.1968   Classification: TS
From: Aesculapius   Ref. no. 2040 QR
To: Minerva
Subject: 51

Dossier 51 is being scrutinized. We shall give it our best attention.

To enable us to make a typological analysis of the subject, we request early information as to the precise width and thickness of the diving-board of the Hilton Hotel swimming-pool in Rabat (photo no. 11 attached to the memorandum relating to ref. 2001 UR)

Date: 6.1.1968
From: Minerva
To: Mercury

Classification: TS
Ref. no. 2041 JW

Provide following information: width and thickness of the diving-board of the Hilton Hotel swimming-pool in Rabat.

We specify that the diving-board in question is the one in photograph no. 11 attached to the memorandum relating to ref. 2001 UR. The photo was taken in June 1963. You will check whether the diving-board has been replaced since that date and, if so, whether the replacement was of the same dimensions.

The matter is urgent.

Date: 8.1.1968
From: Mercury
To: Minerva
Subject: 51

Classification: TS
Ref. no. 2042 MR

Your memo 2034 RA of 30.12.1967 contained four paragraphs extracted from a directive of J 4813 from Jupiter. The first paragraph read as follows:

'I hereby order that all current or projected actions directly or indirectly affecting 51 be suspended until further notice.'

It is consequently not possible for us to proceed in accordance with the request contained in your memo 2041 JW of 6.1.1968.

Date: 9.1.1968   Classification: R
From: Minerva   Ref. no. 2043 BK
To: Mars
Subject: Menelaus

We write to confirm today's conversation. You will inform
Menelaus of the reprimand issued by Jupiter and to be entered
in his personal file. You will reimburse his expenses only as to
one quarter of the amount claimed.

In view of your comment we are prepared to agree that
Menelaus' clumsy behaviour may in some measure be explained
by strain resulting from the difficult missions with which he has
been entrusted during the past year. In consequence, and solely
with the interests of the service in mind, we grant Menelaus a
fortnight's special leave in Morocco.

On return from leave, Menelaus will submit to a medical and
psychological examination AA, on the result of which his future
employment will depend.

Date: 10.1.1968   Classification: TS
From: Hecate   Ref. no. 2044 KP
To: Minerva
Subject: 5353

Screening procedure 3 with regard to 5353 was ordered in Minerva's memo 2023 LS of 11.12.1967.

We approached Clio with a request for the necessary records on 12.12.1967. Having received no reply we repeated our request on 15.12.1967. The file on 5353 was forwarded by Clio on 18.12.67.

A conference with Mercury was held on 13.12.1967. Certain information was communicated to us concerning 5353, including suggestions as to appropriate methods of approach.

After due consideration of these various items of intelligence, we entrusted Hecate 2 with the execution of the procedure requested.

Prior to putting in hand the usual procedure, Hecate 2 contacted the subject on two occasions on 22.12.1967 and 29.12.67.

On 22.12.1967 Hecate 2 made his first approach under concealed identity. His reception was such that he decided to proceed immediately to the second phase of his prearranged plan, particularly as Mercury had reported that 5353's contact had assured them that the preliminary observation specified for screening procedure 3 would lead to no positive results in this case, since 5353 had been under observation by the said contact for six weeks without any positive result being obtained. Hecate 2 informed 5353 that he was ready to pay for intelligence concerning the senior officials with whom she came into contact. 5353 accepted this proposal without enquiring as to the future recipient of such information or as to the use which would be made of it.

114

Hecate 2 made an offer of money which was refused. Another meeting was arranged for 29.12.1967. In the course of this meeting, agreement was reached on the figure by increasing the offer by 10% above the sum originally mentioned by Hecate 2. Hecate 2 stressed that any information must be exclusive and this demand was accepted.

It is thus certain that 5353 is open to exploitation by anyone prepared to pay a sum which is, be it noted, minimal. This fact does not prove that 5353 is at this moment in the pay of a rival service, but it does show that she might be or might at any time become so. Her acceptance of Hecate 2's offer shows that she is prepared to be a double agent and, consequently, perhaps a triple agent.

This early result seems to us to require a reassessment of our arrangements with 5353. The possibility that 5353 is *even now* working for a rival organization cannot be entirely dismissed and must be more closely investigated than is possible by the use of procedure 3, which has been hitherto the only procedure ordered. Only procedure 1 can be considered adequate for such an investigation.

We would add that it is possible that 5353, even although she may or might, in future, be working as a double or triple agent, is possibly operating on a system of water-tight compartments. This is in any case the impression gained by Hecate 2. We think it right that you should receive from us a recording of Hecate 2's verbal report (enclosed herewith) as it will give you more direct insight into 5353's clearly somewhat baffling personality.

In conclusion, we would, however, stress that Hecate 2's supposition that 5353 has adopted a system of water-tight compartments remains his own personal hypothesis and that, failing any more positive intelligence, we find ourselves at the moment unable to endorse this view ourselves.

Enclosure: typescript of a recording of Hecate 2's verbal report

O.K. then I did let you have a bit of a report but you'll see it can all be said in a dozen lines easily/she fell for my spiel hook line and sinker nothing but yes yes yes all the way/queer old girl you know/a sort of great big old grey mare who looks at you as if she'd caught you pinching her jam – a real symphony in grey/ grey eyes grey hair held back with a hair-band grey blouse grey skin grey teeth grey voice/not exactly cheerful as you can imagine/ not the sort who lets her hair down and tells you everything in a passionate embrace/anyway I pretended to be a bloke from the TV to find out what the viewers thought about the programme but I'd've done better to stick to the old story of selling household articles/because my goodness the kitchen she took me into was an absolute symphony in white with full orchestra/it was like being in a shopwindow/fridge cooker with six rings washing-machine washing-up machine automatic potato-peeler and three or four other shiny machines for god knows what not to mention her crippled daughter in her overall a white overall of course sitting knitting in her all-white invalid chair/it's a scream really to think that all the cash she manages to squeeze out of us is invested in a model kitchen/or perhaps it's rather sad really I don't know/the mata haris looked a bit different didn't they/but that's what I think now/ at the time I thought the whole thing was hilarious and as this made me feel cheerful I decided to go straight into the attack head-on/we had a bit of a natter first about the latest serial and about how common one of the female announcers was and then I switched over to all her smashing

116

kitchen equipment and saying excuse me but that must have cost the earth and that she must have a good job to be able to afford things like that/or else I said or else you manage to make a bit on the side/and at that I saw the invalid daughter look up from her knitting seemed kind of interested and a little grey glint came into her mother's grey eye/and then dead silence while I sat smiling in a knowing way/so I drew the conclusion that what I'd said had gone home and so I started talking/mum didn't turn a hair which meant that this wasn't the first time and she came straight back with the 64,000 dollar question how much/just like that no beating about the bush as if I was offering her a four-speed vacuum cleaner with automatic switch-on/I tried a bit of psychology to find out why and how but the only thing which interested her was the cash/so finally I mentioned the figure that we'd agreed on and that led on to a long tale of woe/about her husband who was an alcoholic and good for nothing fortunately he'd been run over by a car five years ago the invalid daughter who wasn't going to live very long according to the doctors but who was still there eating like a horse and the other daughter supposed to be a health visitor but something of a tart apparently whose daily round comes to a sudden halt as soon as she sees a pair of trousers at the door/she got this all off her chest in a crazy sort of way as if it was me who bought her dead husband his first drink starved the fat daughter and deflowered the tart/and then she went on to say she found it quite natural for people to pay to satisfy their fancies and that if it interested me to know what's happening with people who don't concern me then I'd better see if I couldn't stretch it a bit/exactly like an old mother judge who's got nothing against any fancy ideas as long as you don't mind paying for them/a scream isn't it/anyway she's certainly one woman who hasn't been contaminated by romantic ideas/I bet she never reads any spy thrillers/I reckon she thinks we're all a lot of cranks with queer whims like pregnant women and she slips us her stuff thinking it's all very funny really that there are people stupid enough to swap the latest model of a washing machine for old wives' gossip you see what I mean/who called on someone who rang someone who went to bed with someone and so on/so we haggled about the price and as she wouldn't come down we decided to meet again in a week's time so that I could see meanwhile if I could manage to put it up a bit/at the second meeting exactly the same decor plus the health visitor who does seem to have a rather saucy thigh/we went on from where we left off quite openly no inhibitions but my christ talk about no inhibitions the fat daughter putting in her oar and the other one flashing her eyes and making it quite plain that she wouldn't object to a little visit/quite a family I'm telling you/I must say that in all my jobs I've never met any women quite like those/ juppy ought to take them on at an enormous fee to teach our youngsters that you can get information just as well without creeping along under the shadow of a wall or shoving a cork up your arse so that you don't fart/anyway we agreed on my first offer plus ten per cent/not a gold mine as you can see/it's really cut-price intelligence nothing over half-a-dollar/then as we'd agreed I asked about the question of exclusive information/the mother burst out with you're all the same you really are too good to be true and then she said ok/do you really think people are lining up to ask me to tell them all this crap but not really making much of a fuss and sounding very sure of herself she wasn't saying it as if she believed it and I could tell by her face that she was adding up in her mind all the cash she's been getting out of us already to what I was promising her and she was probably calculating whether she could buy herself the latest egg-shelling machine/I let her see that I quite understood that she'd already been supplying one or two other clients and that I was even ready to offer a little bonus if she'd be honest and admit it and that I'd forget all about it and not say another word/but at that she gave me a stony look and shut up sharp/I almost felt as if I'd told a dirty story/to my mind she's just hard-up that's all/she'd be quite capable of handing out information like doing a spot of house-work one hour here two hours somewhere else and why shouldn't everyone be happy like that/of course we could try and put up the stakes really high to be sure of getting exclusive information but I'm not sure that that would work/to my mind she's the sort who prefers lots of little rivers to one big one/apart from the fact that it might be liable to make her nervous she might start asking herself questions/because my opinion is that at the moment she's pretty hazy about it all/I've got the strong impression that she thinks that we're all more or less working privately and that it's

118

all connected with women/so in the end I personally think that I'd go on using her as if nothing had happened but taking good care to check up on her material so as not to make a boob/but of course between that and getting her to bring off something really big that's another matter/but if it's decided to try and go the whole hog you may as well face it straight away it's not going to be money for old rope to get by the three of them/with the invalid sitting there on her fat arse all the time I can't quite see how we can bug the flat/and the mother's not going to be easy either/with all her cleaning jobs and the errands she runs for her employers she must meet twenty or thirty people every day and it'll be bloody difficult to sort them all out/and as for any colleague of mine who has the job of shadowing the health visitor who's offering her fanny all round the town all day well the best of luck that's all I can say/well I think that's about all is there anything you want to ask me

(ends)

Date: 15.1.1968   Classification: TS
From: Minerva   Ref. no. 2046 VG
To: Aesculapius
Subject: 51

Further to your request of 6.1.1968 (ref. no. 2040 QR) we would inform you that the dimensions of the diving-board of the Hilton Hotel swimming pool in Rabat are as follows:

    Width: 21 inches

    Thickness: $2\frac{1}{4}$ inches

Date: 16.1.1968   Classification: TS
From: Minerva   Ref. no. 2047 VC
To: Jupiter
Subject: 51

Please find herewith Hecate's report 2044 KP on 5353 and one enclosure 2045 MG.

While it is true that clearance by screening procedure 1 is an indispensable prerequisite to any intensive use of 5353, in view of the fact that this procedure involves massive deployment of men and material, it would be liable to attract the attention of rival security services. Unless therefore you give specific instructions to the contrary we shall not set screening procedure 1 in operation until Aesculapius has given its diagnosis of 51. Should this diagnosis prove positive, the problem of 5353 would become of secondary importance and no longer offer any urgency.

Enclosures: Hecate's report and enclosure
              Copies for information to Mercury

Date: 12.2.1968   Classification: TS
From: Aesculapius   Ref. no. 2048 BB
To: Minerva
Subject: 51

Report

The subject has been subjected to physiognomical, typological, chirological and graphological analyses.

For the physiognomical, typological and chirological analyses we used photo no. 15 (attached to relevant memorandum 2003 VA) and photo no. 11 (attached to relevant memorandum 2001 UR). The mensurational analysis was based on the dimensions of the diving-board on which 51 was photographed (photo no. 11).

The graphological analysis was based on an original text in 51's handwriting (ref. 1995 OV) and on a photocopy of one of his letters (ref. 1998 JP).

A preliminary synthesis has been produced by combining the relevant elements of the above-mentioned analyses. The diagnosis has been produced by our psychological subsection by combining the synthesis of the external analyses with the character-identity factors deduced from the file.

1. PHYSICAL MEASUREMENTS
   Height: 5ft $8\frac{3}{4}$ inches
   Span: 5ft $10\frac{7}{8}$ inches $+ 1\frac{3}{4}$ inches
   Chest: $34\frac{1}{2}$ inches
   Upper limbs: right $- \frac{7}{8}$
                left $- \frac{7}{8}$
   Lower limbs: $33\frac{1}{4}$ $32\frac{3}{4} + \frac{7}{16}$
   Thorax: 9 $7\frac{1}{2} + 1\frac{5}{16}$
   Abdomen: $11\frac{1}{2}$ $12\frac{1}{8} + \frac{1}{2}$
   Height of sternum: 4 $11\frac{7}{16}$

Head and neck: 11 15/16 12½ + ½
  Average span
  Brachycephalic
  Short neck
  Long thorax
  Short abdomen
  Longibrachial tendency
  Slight macroskelia

2. SYMPTOMATIC TRIAD
  Xiphoid cartilage
    8 lunules of 0.16″
  No independence

3. SPECIAL FEATURES
  Small nose
  Thin mouth
  Markedly hypothenal
  Bushy eyebrows
  Prominent cranial ridge
  Extremely square hands with raised palms

4. HANDWRITING: FEATURES AND TYPES
  Speed: foreshortened, dynamogeniate, lively
  Pressure: sharp, sustained, blobbed, spasmodic, blurred,
               nicked
  Shape: jointed, hooped, full, dissonant, cruciform,
               looped, inharmonious, loose
  Size: upswept, concentrated, ensiform
  Direction: rigid, sloping to the left, slanting backwards,
               retreating, centripetal
  Continuity: blending, excited, combined, organized
  Spacing: sprawling

SUMMARY

A rich and interesting personality. We note a nervous excita-
bility of a spasmodic nature counteracted by a contradictory
mentality stemming from rigidity of judgement, a marked liking
for austerity and overriding psychological barriers.

His mentality is disharmonious, hypersensitive and unstable
with powerful impulses held in check by latent inhibitions. The

subject reacts to external stimuli with vigour but is restrained by a strong super-ego inhibitory complex.

His appearance is sensitive and shy.

On the intellectual level there is real intelligence but combined with an extreme rigour of analytical reasoning. We noted a strong lack of flexibility and a permanent tendency to replace an objective, factual assessment by a mechanical interpretation based on conventional moral or religious standards.

In character, he is well-organized, hard-working and somewhat puritanical. He is distinguished by a rigidity which is counterbalanced by a temperamental hypersensitivity extremely vulnerable, as previously stated, to external stimuli. There ensues a permanent conflict between the stream of externally motivated impulses and the barrier imposed by his character. This dichotomy leads the subject to extremes of behaviour and at the same time gives rise to chronic instability. Mental activity is spasmodic with sudden impulses held in check by the action of inhibitions. We are thus faced by a character sensitive and open whilst at the same time depressed and uncertain and with an inherent latent instability which would be liable to lead to grave psychological disorders but for the subject's basic sense of discipline. Such control is, however, only maintained at the expense of considerable nervous stress which, although showing no apparent physical repercussions at the moment, leads to worry and moodiness, and this permanent self-mutilation gives rise to feelings of frustration which might well develop into a neurosis.

To sum up, the subject has a rich and even involved personality which finds difficulty in accepting its complications and takes refuge from its internal conflicts in emotional reactions of such intensity that they could, in the long run, jeopardize his personality structure by exposing it to dangerous psychological strains.

EXPLOITATION

The question to be answered was the following: would the threat of communicating to his colleagues visual and auditory material compromising for 52 be likely to make 51 exploitable?

It is to be noted that the above working hypothesis takes no account of any psychological trauma liable to be caused in 51 by the brutal revelation of 52's extra-marital sexual relations. We think that this represents a dangerous oversimplification. 51's apparently limited sexuality and the lack of any demonstration of affection which seems to be implied by his correspondence with 52 *in no way* justify the conclusion that he would be able to face up to such visual and aural evidence, which are bound to be traumatic by their very nature, without suffering severe psychological shock. One might indeed interpret these characteristics of 51 as springing from tensions deeply rooted in his marital relationship. In such a hypothesis the trauma inflicted might bring such tensions to breaking-point with consequences that can hardly at this moment of time be predicted. The action which has been suggested rests on a premiss which may be formulated thus: 51's professional interests entirely overshadow his affective life. In view of the lack of any evidence in his file either to confirm or reject this hypothesis, we feel bound to view it with the gravest suspicion until further evidence may become available.

Even should this premiss eventually prove to be justified, it would still remain to be proven that 51's devotion to his profession is such as to make him exploitable.

The character-synthesis outlined above reveals a mentality endowed with an extremely powerful inhibitory mechanism and with the subject responding to external stimuli with highly conformist attitudes based on conventional norms of behaviour. We note the presence of rigid self-control and the existence of behavioural barriers which have hitherto been strong enough to hold his inner compulsions in check. His dossier, although far from exhaustive, confirms the patterns which we have discerned by means of our external analyses. The overall picture is of a character-pattern without exactly defined motivation but reacting with undoubted energy and rigorous principles in one definite direction and consequently unlikely to submit to external pressure; which in fact would have the effect of arousing his inhibitory mechanisms and strengthening his self-imposed discipline.

Prior examination of this file at any other than a most superficial level would moreover have rendered it unnecessary for you to approach Aesculapius and so made superfluous the thorough analysis which we have undertaken at Minerva's request, in accordance with our terms of reference.

It is indeed apparent from the file that a diplomatic incident

125

(the Ben Barka affair) has already resulted in placing 51 in a crisis situation springing from a conflict between the attitude dictated by his ego and that which his superior officers wished him to adopt. The circumstances of the working hypothesis outlined by Minerva were thus realized on this occasion since 51 was faced by the unavoidable decision either to sacrifice his ego to his career or else to sacrifice – or at least to compromise – his career in order to remain true to his ego. The file confirms that the psychological mechanism outlined in the synthesis functioned on that occasion as it probably would in any other, and that 51's 'contradiction-mentality' based on inflexible judgements apparently led him unhesitatingly to sacrifice his professional ambition to what he considered the dictates of his conscience. There is no need to stress how all this practical experience confirms and supports the character-pattern discerned by our objective and subjective analyses of the subject.

We are consequently led to submit the following diagnosis:

1) 51 possesses a rich and even involved personality containing areas which, as a simplification, we would refer to as undefined shadow areas of considerable extent. It is not impossible that these shadow areas (by which we mean internal conflicts, sub-conscious pressures, possible development of neuroses etc.) contain elements likely to make the subject open to exploitation. His file, the compilation of which reveals considerable traces of superficiality and haste, has not provided us with the requisite information to enable us to outline more closely these areas of conflict nor a fortiori to draw up a list of them.

2) Both our theoretical analysis and practical experience indicate that Minerva's working hypothesis is misguided in its premisses and unrealistic in its expectations. Minerva seems to have systematically closed its eyes to the most obvious evidence contained in the file and could hardly have invented any plan less likely to succeed with the subject than the one on which we were asked to comment. In our view it is beyond all doubt that if 51 is subjected to the suggested pressure he would react by reporting it to his superiors and at the same time offering his resignation.

We therefore earnestly advise against the adoption of this plan.

Returned herewith: 34 items and 19 photos

Date: 12.2.1968   Classification: TS
From: Aesculapius   Ref. no. 2049 GO
To: Jupiter
Subject: Minerva

In its memo 2036 BA of 3.1.1968 Minerva requested us to study objective 51 and report on the operation suggested as likely to render him liable to exploitation.

We are today forwarding to Minerva our adverse report based on the detailed analyses to which our different subsections have submitted the file, although it had become apparent to us on our first reading that Minerva's working hypothesis was almost ludicrously inadequate and misguided.

We wish to protest strongly against the irresponsible way in which Aesculapius' time and energy have been wasted at a time when as you are aware heavy demands are being made on us. It will not be possible for us to meet the continually increasing demands of the service if the means available to us to meet such demands prove increasingly inadequate. In presenting such a hastily improvised file for our assessment of so nonsensical a working hypothesis Minerva has certainly not contributed to the efficient functioning of our service as a whole.

Copy for information to Minerva

Date: 13.2.1968 Classification: TS
From: Minerva Ref. no. 2050 VV
To: Jupiter
Subject: 51

Please receive herewith Aesculapius' report 2048 BB on 51.

1 enclosure

Date: 1.2.1968   Classification: TS
From: Mercury   Ref. no. 2051 VD
To: Jupiter
Subject: 51

You have asked us to provide
 1) an analysis of the situation
 2) a plan of operations

1) Aesculapius' report confirms that Operation 51, launched
five months ago, has reached an impasse by reason of the in-
efficient way in which it has been handled. Minerva has refrained
from exploring any avenues of attack except those leading through
52 and 52A, and specifically underestimating the possibilities
opened up by 5353. Since Operation Justine Minerva has
persisted in its course of action instead of profiting from its
failures and launching in new directions. It is to be feared that
this obstinacy is motivated solely by the desire systematically to
frustrate our suggestions. It is significant that since your decisions
taken after Operation Justine, Minerva has preferred to submit
to Aesculapius, with undue haste, an incomplete file in the hope
that its views would be confirmed rather than accept your
assessment of our 'skilful and cautious' handling of 5353 (in this
connection we wish once more to repeat our verbal protests with
regard to Minerva's garbling of the text of your directive J 4813
of 30.12.1967 in its memo 2034 RA of 30.12.1967 addressed to us).

On the operational planning level, Minerva's tactics once
again reveal its inability to adopt the flexible technique of pene-
tration which has amply proved its worth. Minerva has been
trying to discover 51's areas of weakness for the last five months.
We fear that their choice of method is not relevant to the rational

pursuit of the objective but that on the contry it is mdoyaetɪivb a the psychological satisfaction that Minerva has always sought in the use of forcible techniques which are now outmoded by reason both of changes in intelligence methods and of new political developments.

2) In the present state of Operation 51 the only practicable approach is the utilization of 5353.

In your directive J 4813 of 30.12.1967, paras. 4, 5 and 6, you agreed to the intensive use of 5353 subject to two conditions:

a) that no rival security service had been put on its guard by Menelaus' errors, thus leading to a protective screen being placed round 51 and 52;

b) that Hecate's screening of 5353 should have a satisfactory outcome.

As to point (a) the system of selective observations applied to 52 in accordance with your directive has not led to the discovery of any protective measures on the part of rival security services.

As to point (b), whilst admitting that Hecate's report cannot be described as entirely satisfactory, it is not unsatisfactory. It proves that 5353 is prepared to work as a double agent, which does not mean that she is one already. Hecate added that even if she should become one, she would no doubt be working on the principle of water-tight compartments and this is a safeguard.

In accordance with your verbal agreement, we placed 5353 under observation from 15.1.1968 to 1.2.1968. It did not prove possible to install any listening or recording device in her flat, but she has been constantly shadowed during the above-mentioned period. No suspicious contacts have been discovered during that time, since 5353 has not met anyone not connected with her professional activity.

It would thus appear both from Hecate's report and from our own investigations that there is no objective evidence to suggest that 5353 is at the moment controlled by any rival intelligence organization. This fact does not invalidate Hecate's comments as to the long-term desirability of submitting 5353 to screening procedure 1, but it does justify her short-term employment, assuming that certain elementary security precautions can be guaranteed.

In consequence of this, we submit a project for Operation Zephyr for your approval, as outlined in the enclosed document.

Enclosure: Project for Operation Zephyr
Copies for information to Minerva

Project for
Operation Zephyr

Objective

In our memo 2019 DM of 11.12.1967 we reported that 51 takes files home with him from the office.

In our memo 2028 UA of 21.12.1967 we pointed out that these files were probably those required for the preparation of 51's weekly report on the Quai d'Orsay.

Observation of 51's villa has disclosed that on Thursday evenings the light in his study remains on until different times but always until a late hour.

Despite repeated requests from her contact, 5353 has not been able to discover what kind of work 51 is doing at home. Before 14.1.1968, the opportunity offered on 24.11.1967 did not arise again, since 51 has always been up by the time 5353 arrives at the villa; while since 14.1.1968, the presence of 52, 53, 54 and 55 in the house has removed all possibility of 5353's gaining access to the documents. In any case, 5353 must be considered as unsuited to provide an exact description of documents beyond her intellectual grasp.

As Operation 51 stands at the moment, one urgent and basic objective is to discover what kind of documents 51 takes home every Thursday evening, the sort of work he does during the early part of the night and finally to decide whether the documents and this work are of a routine diplomatic nature or whether, on the other hand, they are concerned with 51's reports to the Quai d'Orsay. In the second case, it would be possible to envisage an indirect exploitation of 51 and to explore the possibility of a permanent contact of this nature.

Such is the proposed target of Operation Zephyr.

Local Conditions

The situation at Delphi has changed to our detriment with regard to the employment of 5353 since 51's wife, children and domestic servant arrived to join him on 14.1.1968. It was to be feared that 55's arrival might bring about a radical change in the situation in that, since 52 has a full-time domestic help, she might decide to dismiss 5353. Such an eventuality has not yet transpired but the fact remains that the presence of five persons in the villa instead of one leaves less room for manoeuvre. For this reason, Mercury deplores the fact that during the months that have elapsed since its memo of 11.12.1967 and the arrival of 51's family, no advantage was taken of the more favourable circumstances to achieve the object now proposed in the Zephyr operation. In apportioning the blame for this, it must be stressed that this failure followed on Operation Justine, which was improvised by Minerva and carried out by Mars in circumstances making it necessary for Jupiter to take certain security measures and particularly to restrict the employment of 5353 until after investigation by Hecate.

Means

5353 and her contact 5672 must be considered incapable of assessing 51's documents or memoranda on a single reading.

5353 is not capable of handling a photo-copying camera. Even should we approach her to suggest teaching her this skill – a course which 5672 considers inadvisable – and if she accepted, she would have no chance of operating during her working hours.

5672 is competent to photograph the documents and memoranda. The problem will be to provide access to them in circumstances offering an acceptable security risk.

With his agreement, we have drawn up a plan offering a maximum chance of success with a minimum of risk.

Our proposal is based on the following observations:

The door of 51's villa is provided with a safety-chain. While 51 was alone in the house, this chain was not used, but 5353 reports that since the arrival of 52 and her children, this chain has been attached every night. As a result, it is impossible to introduce 5672 into the villa during night-time.

On Monday and Wednesday mornings, 51 leaves the villa

133

twenty to twenty-five minutes earlier than on the other days in order to take 53 and 54 to their schools in the official car provided by the French Embassy. On Tuesdays, Thursdays and Fridays, 52 drives the children to school in their private car. She then goes on to a riding-school situated in the suburbs of Delphi and goes riding until roughly 1200 hrs.

We anticipate introducing 5672 into the villa one Thursday morning while 52 is riding. At a time agreed upon in advance by 5672 and 5353, the latter will send 55 off on some errand or other, thus leaving 5353 alone in the villa. In order not to arouse suspicion (an unlikely risk, incidently, in a sparsely populated residential district), 5672 will assume the identity of a plumber.

The villa has five cellars, only one of which is in use. 5672 will move into one of the other four and lock himself in (the keys are in the key-holes of the various doors).

At 0400 hrs on the night of Thursday to Friday, 5672 will leave the cellar and go to 51's study to commence operations. Since 51's and 52's bedroom is a long way from the study, any chance of their being awakened by 5672 is reduced to a minimum. The room immediately above the office is 53's and 54's bedroom, and in view of their extreme youth, the chances of their being awakened are even less. There is the possibility that 51 or 52 may get up for some reason or another but it would seem unlikely that they should decide to go downstairs to the study. We assess such a risk as virtually non-existent.

On completing his task, 5672 will return to the cellar.

5353 will arrange for him to leave the villa on Friday morning in the same way as he entered it on Thursday.

In co-operation with Mars, a security screen will be placed round the villa throughout the night.

We propose 28.3.1968 as the date for Operation Zephyr.

Mercury has sent us 'for information' the plan of an Operation
Zephyr drawn up by itself. We protest against this completely
unacceptable encroachment on Minerva's sphere of activity, since
our terms of reference lay down quite specifically that the planning and control of all operations, of whatever nature, are the
exclusive prerogative of Minerva.

We wish further to refute Mercury's accusation relating to the
delay in making use of intelligence supplied by 5353. It is not
correct that this delay was a result of the instructions contained
in your directive J 4813 issued after Operation Justine. It was due
to the screening process undertaken by Hecate on this agent, in
accordance with your request, a request justified on this, as
indeed on every occasion, when an agent's performance suddenly
improves in quality or in quantity.

Copy for information to Mercury

Date: 26.2.1968　　　　　　　Classification: TS
From: Minerva　　　　　　　Ref. no. 2054 DP
To: Jupiter
Subject: 51

We feel bound to make the following comments on the plan for
Operation Zephyr:

1) Mercury's operational plan depends on an agent, 5353, who
has been described by Hecate as of dubious value.

2) The execution of the project is to be entrusted to an agent
5672, who has never hitherto been used in any active operation.

3) The choice of 5672 is particularly unfortunate in that his
long service in Delphi is liable to have attracted the attention of
the local intelligence services and this would mean that we should
be involved were the operation to miscarry in any way.

4) Mercury's plan contains three technical flaws:

a) the fact that four cellars have not hitherto been used does
not necessarily imply that they may not be used at any moment;

b) there is no guarantee that 55 will be successfully neutralized;

c) the timing of 5672's operation offers considerable risks in
that there seems to be no available evidence as to the time
when 51 will complete his work on the night of Thursday 28th
to Friday 29th March.

5) Even should Operation Zephyr achieve its objective, the
results would not justify the risk involved. At best it would
provide proof that 51 writes his confidential report at his home.
But this information would still leave the major problem unsolved
as to how to obtain *regular* access to the report. *A weekly
Operation Zephyr is both unthinkable and impracticable.*

Date: 4.3.1968   Classification: TS
From: Minerva   Ref. no. 2055 VQ
To: Jupiter
Subject: 51

In a memorandum 5482 BT of 1.3.1968 for general circulation, Hecate reports that the Persian Oribasis passed through Rome/ Fiumicino airport on 29.2.1968. Destination unknown.

We have requested Hecate to supply the appropriate background information, a copy of which is enclosed. Oribasis' previous period of service in Delphi renders it necessary to consider the possibility that he has been entrusted with a new mission here.

This possibility, although we may be unable to verify it immediately for practical reasons, suggests that we should suspend all operations involving 5353 until this agent has been subjected to screening procedure 1.

Enclosure: report on Oribasis

Classification: TS
Ref. no. 2056 PK

Report on Oribasis

Oribasis, born 9.4.1930. Presumed place of birth Cyropolis. First recorded in 1958 as deputy to Diacires in Delphi but some intelligence reports suggest that he had been in the Persian Security Service since 1954 and that he had first of all worked in the Xerxes section of the Central Office. On 15.1.1962 he was reported by our intelligence (reliability A1) as arriving at Paris/ Orly. In the spring of 1962, he was reported as passing through Quebec, Montreal and Winnipeg. He stayed in Winnipeg from 14.3.1962 to 23.4.1962. Intelligence (reliability B2) reports him as being the leader of the Livak operation (one dead). On 15.6.1963, he led the commando which kidnapped Alcibiades, leader of a Mars team. He himself interrogated and then disposed of Alcibiades (v. our interrogation ref. 2250 JP of the Persian agent Nabdates). Mars received Jupiter's permission for an Operation Nemesis. The Alcibiades section was given the task of liquidating Oribasis. Oribasis survived the two attempts on his life (7.1.1964 and 30.8.1964), killing our agents 2731 and 4480. Agent 7485 reported that Oribasis was said to have received a bullet wound in his right side on 30.8.1964. From 1.1.1965 to 3.9.1966, Oribasis was attached to the central office as Cyrus' first deputy, but the repercussions caused by Cyrus' suicide are said to have made him ask to be reposted to the Persian Ops Section. A most reliable source reported his presence in Delphi from 18.11.1966 to 29.4.1967. He is known to have arrived in Nigeria on 5.5.1967 and to have been responsible for the incidents at Babouele. In June 1967, he was reliably reported as still living in Nigeria, but an A2 source reported that he was the leader of the Valeri operation in Carthage on 8.6.1967 (one dead) and of the Torresgrosa operation on 30.6.1967. The Operation Nemesis launched against him on 2.8.1963 was called off by Jupiter's directive J 7430 of 24.8.1966 after the capture of our agent 9101 at Persepolis, when an agreement was made with the Persians whereby 9101, although condemned to death, would not be executed as long as Oribasis remained alive.

Operation Zephyr will take place on 28.3.1968 on the lines proposed by Mercury.

Mercury will explain to Minerva why we have decided to ignore the objections raised by Minerva in its memo 2054 DP of 26.2.1968 against Operation Zephyr.

Copy for information to Mercury

Date: 5.3.1968   Classification: R
From: Minerva   Ref. no. 2057 BK
To: Mars
Subject: Menelaus

Summon Menelaus without delay. Top priority.

Note that Menelaus will not be available from 6.3.1968 to 27.3.1968 inclusive.

Date: 7.3.1968   Classification: TS
From: Mercury   Ref. no. 2058 VB
To: Minerva
Subject: Operation Zephyr

Further to Jupiter's directive ref. J 2720 of 5.3.1968, we hereby inform you of the reasons which induced us to disregard the objections which you felt it necessary to raise concerning Operation Zephyr.

The mission entrusted to 5672, 5353's contact, does not seem to us to come under the heading of an operational activity. We are convinced that 5672 will carry out Operation Zephyr more efficiently than the Mars specialists undertook Operation Justine, and that no identification of 5672 by rival intelligence services will arise should any incident lead to his discovery by them.

Moreover, it must not be forgotten that 5672 has been 5353's contact for some years. It is for this reason that 5353 has agreed to take part in Operation Zephyr, which lies outside her normal activities. 5672 is of the opinion, an opinion which we share, that 5353 would refuse to collaborate with a stranger.

The three technical objections which you raised are not valid. It is unlikely that the four unused cellars should suddenly and quite by chance be brought into use on the very day that 5672 is hiding there. As for 55's neutralization by 5353, this presents no risk since by reason of her age and the fact that she is a local woman, 5353 exercises considerable authority over 55 and tells her what to do. Finally, the time at which 51 finishes his work presents no problem because if 5672 sees any light under the office door he will return to the cellar and wait for a further period of time.

Your criticism of the subsequent exploitation of 51 should

Operation Zephyr be successfully concluded seems prima facie more reasonable, but only because of your persistent failure to make a proper assessment of Mercury's efforts.

In para. 3 of your memo 2007 VA of 10.11.1967, you urged that contact be maintained between 8956 and 55. In pursuance of this policy, a permanent association has been formed including full and satisfactory sexual intercourse dating from 31.12.1967. Shortly before her departure for Delphi, 55 assured 8956 on a number of occasions that she was ready to leave 52's service and remain in Paris if he would promise to marry her. On our instructions, 8956 has remained non-committal, but not discouraging, on this subject. Since 55's arrival in Delphi, her letters to 8956 prove that she would be ready to return to marry him. We have ordered 8956 to continue to offer further encouragement to this attitude.

Our working hypothesis is the following: if Operation Zephyr provides confirmation that 51 writes his confidential reports at home, 8956 will write to 55 on our instructions telling her that he is ready for her to join him. 52 will then be faced by a domestic crisis, since 5353's help alone will not be sufficient to enable her to run the household. She will ask 5353 to work for her full-time, living in. 5353 will refuse, but will suggest that 52 might engage her daughter, who is a health visitor at the moment. In view of the scarcity of servants in Delphi, it is certain that 52 will accept. With 5353's daughter permanently installed in 51's home, we shall have guaranteed regular access to 51's reports. We would point out that 5353's daughter has already agreed to this arrangement, providing certain financial conditions are fulfilled. These conditions, although onerous, are acceptable to Jupiter in view of the importance of the issues involved.

Not only does our hypothesis not exclude degree 1 screening of 5353, it also involves screening 5353's daughter as well, since she will become an essential cog in our whole mechanism.

It seems to us impossible, however, to put off Operation Zephyr until such time as the screening of these agents, and particularly of 5353, has been completed. It would be pointless to arrange for 55 to be called back to Paris with all the obligations that would ensue for 8956 and to arrange for 5353's daughter to be engaged by 52, if it eventually turned out that the work which 51 takes home on Thursday has no connexion with his confidential reports. This is why in our outline proposal for Operation Zephyr we pointed out that our basic objective was to ascertain this precise fact. But while this is possible at the present time, thanks to 5353's co-operation, the situation may well change overnight. In point of fact, 5353 has informed us that 52 had warned her, soon after her arrival in Delphi, that she intended to continue to employ her only until 55 had settled in. While no exact date was fixed, it was understood that this would take a few weeks. On our instructions, 5353 succeeded in putting off the date of her dismissal, which has still not been fixed, largely because 5353 has been aided and abetted by 55, who is obviously in no hurry to find herself having to cope with all the housework alone. 5353 may, however, be dismissed at any moment, and it would be disastrous for this to happen before we have ascertained for certain the nature of the work that 51 does in his office at home. This is why, in our outline proposal for Operation Zephyr, we pointed out that it was *urgent* to ascertain this precise fact.

As for the Persian Oribasis' departure for an unknown destination (v. your memo 2055 VQ of 4.3.1968 to Jupiter) this does not seem to us to represent a sufficient reason for cancelling or delaying Operation Zephyr. We share Jupiter's view that our activities should not be paralysed every time Oribasis takes it into his head to board a plane.

Date: 9.3.1968   Classification: TS
From: Mercury   Ref. no. 2059 CP
To: Jupiter
Subject: Operation Zephyr

In the course of a conference held today, Minerva and Mars informed us of the proposed arrangements to throw a protective screen round 51's villa during the nights of 28.3.1968 to 29.3.1968.

Minerva refused to make the slightest modification in the plan which they had drawn up with Mars, despite our objections against the excessive deployment of personnel (the Epaminondas section with four vehicles) and against their instructions to remain in close proximity to the objective. These measures strike us as highly unsuitable in a sparsely inhabited residential district where they are liable to attract attention, even at night.

In these circumstances, we are of the opinion that it is not possible to carry out Operation Zephyr with adequate certainty of success. We ask to be relieved of this mission.

Date: 11.3.1968   Classification: TS
From: Jupiter   Ref. no. J 8010
To: Minerva
Subject: Operation Zephyr

Mercury is hereby given full and entire responsibility for Operation Zephyr. All requisite decisions for the preparation and execution of the operation will come under its sole authority.

Copy for information to Mercury

Date: 20.3.1968   Classification: TS
From: Minerva   Ref. no. 2060 MW
To: Hecate
Subject: Aesculapius

In accordance with article 38 (Internal Administrative Regulations) we wish to report the following facts:

On 19.3.1968 at 1145 hrs approx. Minerva 3 received a telephone call in his office from a colleague in Aesculapius. This colleague informed him that he belonged to the psychological subsection and that he was a member of the team which had provided the diagnosis of dossier 51. He added that he would like to have a private chat with Minerva 3 on this matter and invited him to have lunch with him on that day. Aware of the infringement of regulations involved in this action (personal contact between two colleagues from different sections without permission from a superior official, and the suggestion that a matter should be discussed 'privately'), Minerva 3 refused the invitation to go out to lunch, but being anxious to identify the official from Aesculapius and discover the motives behind his proposal, Minerva 3 suggested that he should call on him at his (i.e. Minerva 3's) office.

The official from Aesculapius called on Minerva 3 at 1230 hrs on that same day. Minerva 3 described him as follows: approximate age: 35 years; approximate height and weight: 5′ 9″ and 180 lbs; hair: light brown receding on the forehead; eyes: dark brown; tortoiseshell spectacles; nose: short and slightly upturned; mouth: wide and thick lips; a scar $1\frac{1}{2}″$ to $1\frac{3}{4}″$ long under the right ear; chin with deep central cleft; pale grey suit, black bow-tie with red spots, black shoes with thick soles, slight lisp, has

147

nervous tic, occasional fits of sniffing for no apparent reason. His telephone extension number was 810.

At the beginning of the conversation, Minerva 3 switched on his built-in tape recorder. We attach herewith the typescript of the recorded conversation.

1 enclosure

Aesculapius	Do I disturb you
Minerva 3	Not a bit/take a seat/the trouble is that I've got to hold the fort and so I can't get away/we're expecting an important report to come in any minute/it's ok it looks broken but it's not
Ae	Your special task I suppose
M3	What special task
Ae	Why 51 of course
M3	You're quite wrong there/he's not the only person we're taking care of you know/anyway what makes you think that's one of my jobs (Ae laughs)
Ae	Rules are rules eh/it's true that I'm not supposed to know but the whole business has stirred up quite a fuss with us/we've been looking into it very carefully before deciding who's for the chop/you've still got quite a few friends amongst the old hands but it's the young 'uns who've had their way/they're on mercury's side don't make any mistake about it/they couldn't resist the temptation of giving you the knock on the way/you must agree it wasn't a chance to be missed I've hardly ever seen a lousier report I promise you and I've seen some pretty punk ones in my time/is that an ash-tray/thanks what on earth possessed you/a sudden masochistic

urge/a deep yearning for a kick up the arse
(5 seconds silence)
(Ae laughs)

Ae   Don't look like that old boy/they're not going
to sack the whole lot of minerva/our local
grapevine has it that it's your boss who's for the
high jump/mercury's had his knife into him ever
since the gilman business and now all that remains is for old juppy to give it a twist/the atmosphere must be a bit tense in your outfit isn't it

M3   Not particularly/we can't spare the time/we just
get on with our job that's all/once in a while we
make a balls-up like everybody else and if they
want to discipline us all we can do is to grin and
bear it and hope to keep our noses clean in future

Ae   Splendid my dear fellow absolutely splendid I
can see that you've got a brilliant career in front
of you if you can manage to control your
complexes

M3   look if you've come here trying to be funny

Ae   Of course not old man of course not

M3   And for christ's sake blow your nose can't you
you keep on sniffing it's getting on my nerves

Ae   keep calm old boy keep calm relax/there there/
naturally I expected to find you all a bit keyed-
up/ok I'll not say any more not a word/anyway
you know that anything I said was just by way
of a bit of gossip/your little squabbles with
mercury are no concern of mine I assure you/
my own little job keeps me quite busy enough
thank you/did you read our report on 51

M3   Of course

Ae   And you took it seriously
(4 seconds silence)

M3   Of course I did

Ae   That was really nice of you/it's wonderful to
discover that there are still people who take us
seriously/cigarette/so when you read for example that 51's handwriting was dynamogeniate

ensiform fornicational and upyourpipeable you
clapped your hand to your brow and exclaimed
eureka

M3   May I point out that my terms of reference do
not include any assessment of what value
Aesculapius' work may or may not have

Ae   And the measurements/most enlightening eh
measurements/I'm sure that the height of the
sternum opened your eyes to lots of things/what
a joke/shall I tell you the only important
measurement there is it's the thing that set of
jokers doesn't worry about of course/the penis
my dear chap yes old man it's the penis of
course/tell me the length of a man's penis and
I'll analyse him in two shakes of a lamb's tail
with a ninety per cent chance of being right/that
makes you laugh/take your 51's well-known
compatriot/napoleon bonaparte had about the
size of my little finger and a couple of balls about
as big as a ten-year-olds/so you see my dear
chap I can tell you that his whole career was
made by that penis and those balls I'm telling
you he spent his whole life making it longer and
making them bigger/symbolically of course you
understand/his army was his sexual organ which
he rammed up his women who were called
austria spain england russia/but that last one
had a vagina a bit too big for him/he paddled
about in the russian vagina like that other little
corporal a century and a half later/and as for
him old chap I have a strong suspicion that but
for that can of petrol at the end they wouldn't
have found 'enough in his breeks to make eva's
pussy give a little miaow the poor dear/he must
have had a few problems round the pubic area
too old boy/so he transferred it all onto the
wehrmacht an armoured division old chap that's
a pretty good sexual substitute isn't it/and what
about all those famous strategic retreats isn't

151

that just like the sex act to and fro to and fro
I'm telling you old man that it would be not only
possible but easy to work out a complete system
of symbols just from that and I'm going to let
you into a secret I'm not sure that I won't throw
up this job one day quite soon so that I can do
just that

(a series of hissing sounds that can be interpreted as the fits of sniffing mentioned by
Minerva 3)

M3   So what you're saying is that we were entirely
          wrong not to let you know the size of 51's penis

Ae   You're pulling my leg but I do assure you that
          it would have been a bloody sight more interest-
          ing than all that crap that you had in the file/do
          you know we had three psychiatrists on the job/
          we really did take a lot of trouble you know/but
          there was nothing solid to chew on/so the diag-
          nosis had to be based primarily on the synthesis
          of our analysis of external factors and all those
          friends of yours in our department couldn't
          resist the temptation of having a go at you

M3   You've already told me that/what's the point of
          repeating it

Ae   Because it really makes me feel sick to see you
          fall for a stupid trick like that/as a matter of
          fact your 51 was not a bad subject at all really/
          I'd even go so far as to say he's a nice little man
          full of possibilities/of course you haven't made
          proper use of them but that doesn't alter the fact
          that they're there

M3   You mean the famous shadow areas I suppose/
          come in/thanks put it down there

Ae   Well my dear chap it's nearly one o'clock and
          I've got a gastric ulcer that needs feeding at
          regular intervals so we won't waste our time
          talking about light and shade/I merely came
          along to tell you this/amongst all that tripe in the
          file there's one item that really made me think/a

photo that your bloke keeps in his wallet/a photo of some sort of woman/rather crumpled and messed about according to the description I mean the photo not the woman/it had even been torn up and stuck together again/that's interesting in itself isn't it/but what really made me sit up was that there are two holes in the place of the eyes/you remember/and doesn't that remind you of something old chap/doesn't it really/haven't you ever heard of those fetishist rites/the photos that you prick with pins those little wax figures that you stick through where the heart should be so as to kill the bloke or the woman that it represents/that surprises you eh/ that doesn't hang together with your idea of 51/ but that's exactly what's so interesting old chap/ so I simply came along to suggest to you/don't let it go any further will you/it's not really in order what I'm doing so don't start shouting it over the house-tops/to suggest that you might scratch around a bit round that woman/when you've finished let me know and come and tell me what you've discovered about her

M3   Plus the size of 51's penis of course

Ae   Don't worry that woman will lead you straight to the penis/if you want to ring me I'm extension 810/I must go/lovely to have had such a nice chat with you

M3   Me too/I hope your ulcer feels hungry

Ae   He eats like a horse old man/to be absolutely complete there's another item in the file which put an idea into my mind but it's all rather vague at the moment and I'd sooner keep it to myself if you don't object/cheerio and see you soon I hope

M3   Goodbye/and thanks

(ends)

1) In your directive J 2720 of 5.3.1968 you fixed the date of the
above operation for 28.3.1968.

2) In accordance with our instructions, Achilles has been sent
to Delphi and contacted 5353 on 24.3.1968 at 1800 hrs. Achilles
introduced himself to 5353 as having been sent by Hecate 2 as a
result of a previous agreement in principle already reached
between Hecate 2 and 5353. He told 5353 that Hecate 2 wished
to obtain information as to the people frequented by a certain
high official at Delphi in whose house 5353 works as a cleaner two
afternoons a week. He showed 5353 three photos and asked her
if she had at any time seen any of the three men in her employer's
house. 5353 replied in the negative. Achilles asked if 5353 would
keep a check on the visits her employer received and note the
dates and times when the three men called on him. He added that
it was not possible for him to leave the photos behind with 5353
and advised her to write down the description of the three men.
5353 assured him that she had an excellent memory but when
Achilles pressed her she agreed to note down the descriptions. In
accordance with his instructions, Achilles refrained from helping
her to do this and learned by heart the wording of the notes
written down by 5353 in his presence. Here is the complete text
transmitted to us by W/T from Achilles: 'An almost bald man
with long hair at the back and no tie – a man with wavy hair and
black specs, so you can't see his eyes – a man smiling with
wrinkles and a feather in his hat.'

3) In accordance with our instructions, on 25.3.1968 at 1045

hrs Menelaus called at 51's house posing as a commercial traveller. He has sent us a W/T message stating that he saw no chain or special safety device on the villa door.

4) From information gathered locally by Menelaus, it appears that on 28.3.1968 the Italian Embassy at Delphi is giving an official dinner-party followed by a dance. 51 and 52 have replied accepting the invitation which was sent them.

These facts lead us to make the following appraisal:

1) Attached to Mercury's memo 1991 NB of 10.11.1967 is a list of items from 51's wallet, alleged to have been made by 5353 on 2.11.1967 (cf. item 8, ref. 1999 HN). This list was so remarkable for the accuracy of its descriptions that 5353 was congratulated on it by Mercury and granted a merit bonus. It was the first of a series of intelligence reports whose increasing interest decided us to subject 5353 to a Hecate screening process. It will be as apparent to you as it has been to us that the three descriptions written down by 5353 in Achilles' presence bear no resemblance, as far as technical quality is concerned, to the list of items in 51's wallet alleged to have been made by this same 5353 (the comparison is the more striking since this list also involved describing a number of photographs). This observation raises the question as to who can have helped 5353 in drawing up the list and with what purpose.

2) Acting on 5353's statement that the front door of 51's villa was secured by a safety-chain at night, Mercury plans to introduce 5672 into the building on the morning of 28.3.1968 and arrange for him not to leave until the following morning. In view of the fact that it is only possible to throw a protective screen round the villa during the hours of darkness, it will follow that 5672 will remain unprotected during the whole of the day of the 28th as well as during the morning of the 29th. This fact must give rise to grave concern when it is remembered that it is a consequence of false intelligence from 5353 as to the existence of a safety-chain.

3) 51's and 52's presence at the dinner-dance at the Italian Embassy eliminates the possibility of 51's working in the evening of 28.3.1968, so that in any case Operation Zephyr cannot achieve its aim on the date planned. This observation raises the subsidiary question as to whether the date of 28.3.1968 was arranged by

155

Mercury at 5353's instigation and whether this choice represents an attempt by agents possibly controlling 5353 to encourage us to embark on an operation at a time when 51's and 52's absence will facilitate their own countermeasures.

In conclusion, we consider that it is possible that we have been involved in an attempt to compromise us, in three stages:

a) a propaganda campaign by a service controlling 5353 to enhance her importance in our eyes. This campaign was launched four months ago with the list of items from 51's wallet and culminated in the as yet unconfirmed intelligence that 51 took files home with him on Thursday evenings

b) a false description of the premises by 5353 with the object of introducing one of our agents into the house with insufficient security precautions

c) the choice of a date leaving the coast clear for a rival service to take countermeasures on the night of 28th/29th March, if this rival service had decided not to act during the hours of daylight for the same reasons as will prevent us from providing an adequate protective screen either during the day of 28.3.1968 or during the morning of the 29th.

These observations lead us to put forward the following proposals:

1) That Operation Zephyr be cancelled.

2) That Mercury be once more and henceforth restricted to its executive capacity as laid down in its terms of reference.

3) That a Dead Leaves operation be started against 51.

We are convinced that these suggestions will be in accordance with your own conclusions and will receive your assent. Should this not be so, since we will then find it impossible to continue fulfilling our functions in circumstances that we consider abnormal and dangerous, we shall be forced, in the best interests of the service, to request permission to report to the Supreme Authority.

Date: 26.3.1968   **Classification:** TS
From: Jupiter   **Ref. no. J 5224**
To: Minerva
Subject: 51

1) Operation Zephyr is hereby cancelled.

2) An Operation Dead Leaves against 51 is authorized with immediate effect.

Copy for information to Mercury

Date: 27.3.1968
From: Minerva
To: Mercury
Subject: 51

Classification: TS
Ref. no. 2063 DM

1) An Operation Dead Leaves is herewith launched against 51.

2) You are to detach the appropriate staff and set in train the necessary routine operations. You are to inform us in advance of any action you propose to take. Any results are to be transmitted to us immediately as available.

3) You are to arrange for 8956 to bring 55 back to Paris according to our provisional plan in the event of Operation Zephyr's success. 5353 is to try to have 55 replaced by her daughter. 8956 will interrogate 55 to discover 51's and 52's social and other contacts in Delphi.

4) One essential target will be to identify and to try to trace the woman whose photo is partly described under item 10 of the list of contents of 51's wallet drawn up by 5353 (enclosure 1999 HN in your memo 1991 NB of 10.11.1967).

5) You are immediately to begin investigating every person who appears in the file as having contact with 51 and/or 52, with the exception of 52A.

6) The choice of Operation Dead Leaves is intended to avoid arousing any suspicion on the part of the French security services. Any investigation of 51's professional contacts is forbidden.

Date: 27.3.1968
From: Minerva
To: Venus
Subject: Operation Jumping

Classification: TS
Ref. no. 2064 RG

1) You will select a male agent possessing the following qualities:
    marked virility
    sadistic potentiality
    horseman
    a man of the world.

2) His task will be to form an association with a person allotted the code-number 52. Contact will be established at a riding-school frequented by the woman concerned.

3) Mercury will supply you with all the necessary routine details.

4) The operation will be given the code-name Jumping.

Copy for information to Mercury

Date: 27.3.1968
From: Minerva
To: Hecate
Subject: 5353

Classification: TS
Ref. no. 2065 LS

Apply screening procedure 1 to the above agent, to include her
immediate family circle.

My dear colleague,

I find it very hard to reply. You must admit that your query is
most embarrassing. I could tell you, of course, that we in Aesculapius find this particular colleague rather a queer fish, something
of an eccentric, but since the whole of our organization finds
Aesculapius in general rather peculiar, this wouldn't help you
very much. Let's say then, if you like, that he is even more peculiar
than the rest of us.

His unexpected visit to Minerva 3 doesn't really surprise me.
His grasp of regulations is so vague and he's not in the least
interested in sticking to them. Hecate was obliged to take him to
task three or four years ago, although in the end things were
patched up. As a matter of fact, he is an extremely interesting
person, but his character is subject to anarchical impulses which
he seems quite unable to control, and is liable to deviate into
completely aberrant behaviour. Some of my colleagues have
often strongly urged me to have him given deep psycho-analytical
treatment. It cannot be denied that there is more than a hint of
obsessional neurosis. However, I've always been against such a
suggestion because it would only mean that Aesculapius would
have to embark on a policy of self-analysis which would in turn
mean spending our whole time examining each other in order to
reach the quite obvious conclusion that we are all mad, like
everybody else (I'm simplifying, of course, because the scientific
definition of madness would require a great deal of explanation
that we can't go into here). My own attitude has always been that

the psychoses and neuroses of the various members of my staff are in themselves not really harmful as long as they can fit into the normal running of the service and make it more efficient.

Having said this, I can't warn you too strongly against blindly accepting anything he may have said. You didn't feel it necessary to give me any idea of what his conversation with Minerva 3 was about, and indeed I've neither the right nor any particular desire to hear about it. But I do think that it's indispensable for you to know that whilst my colleague has on occasion shown flashes of genuinely original and illuminating insight, I could also quote you many other examples where his conduct was completely misguided and misleading.

You ought therefore to take everything he says with extreme caution. I would earnestly advise you not to undertake any action before discussing it with us previously, so that we may apply the necessary correctives that we alone are competent to judge appropriate to his conclusions or suggestions.

You asked me for my opinion and I have given you it. You asked me, specifically, to give my personal opinion as a friend. I don't need to tell you how ready and willing I always am to respond to such an appeal. But it is a fact that in the last few days our whole organization has been pervaded by an atmosphere of red-tape and fuss about regulations not unconnected with your department, and I also have the impression that Hecate is beginning to show interest in us once again, probably as a result of our colleague's unfortunate visit to Minerva 3. As a result of all this, I feel sure that you will understand my request that you place this letter on the file in accordance with our regulations.

Sincerely yours,
Aesculapius

Minerva's ref. 2066 PP

Date: 30.3.1968   Classification: TS
From: Mercury   Ref. no. 2067 EF
To: Minerva
Subject: DL 51

1) A preliminary series of investigations has been undertaken with the purpose of identifying, locating and where possible contacting the persons whose names appear in the file, viz:

Hervé X (letter 1994 ZA from 51 to 52)
Simone X (ditto)
Mme Marcelle X (letter 1998 JB from 51 to 53)
Honoré X (ditto)
Mme d'Etchandart (ditto)
M. Nauvois (ditto)
Jean-François X (list of contents of wallet ref. 1999 HN)
M. and Mme Roldoire (ditto)
Dr H. Allix (ditto)
Mme Lieuvert (ditto)
M. and Mme Durand (letter ref. 2038 MM from 52 to 51)
Thérèse X (ditto)
Janou Lefèvre (ditto)
Dr Le Noir (ditto)
Jacky X (ditto)
Delattre (ditto)

2) This list does not include members of 51's and 52's respective families, who are currently being separately investigated.

3) Research has been put in train to discover persons having been in contact with 51 at the institutions and units mentioned in the records file, viz:

Ecole Saint-Patrice, 8 Rue Cassette (Paris VI)
Collège Ladislas, 19 Rue de Fleurus (Paris VI)

163

Institute of Political Studies, 27 Rue Saint-Guillaume
(Paris VI)

Ecole Nationale d'Administration, 56 Rue des Saints-Pères
(Paris VI)

24th I.T.R.

O.T.R. Cherchell

117th I.R.

4) Orders have been given to 8956 to ensure 55's speedy return
to Paris.

Date: 2.4.1968
From: Minerva
To: Mercury
Subject: DL 51

Classification: TS
Ref. no. 2068 BF

1) In para. 6 of our memo 2063 DM of 27.3 1968 it was specifically stated: 'The choice of Operation Dead Leaves is intended to avoid arousing any suspicion on the part of the French security services. Any investigation of 51's professional contacts is forbidden.'

By reason of the high proportion of former pupils of the Institute of Political Studies (Public Service Section), and of the Ecole Nationale d'Administration, who occupy official positions, the above-mentioned ban is extended to these two institutions.

2) It is not necessary to investigate Janou Lefèvre, to whom incidental reference is made in letter 2038 MM from 52 to 51. Janou Lefèvre is a female member of the French Olympic Riding Team.

Date: 2.4.1968   Classification: TS
From: Mercury   Ref. no. 2069 OV
To: Minerva
Subject: Operation Zephyr

Following the cancellation of Operation Zephyr, we send you
herewith the results of investigations undertaken at our request
by 5672, our contact with 5353:

1) The list of contents of 51's wallet (ref. 1999 HN) was not
drawn up solely by 5353. According to explanations given to
5672, it appears that 5353 found the wallet at about 0900 hrs
on 2.11.1967. She at once made a summary list of its contents.
About one hour later, her daughter, the health visitor, who happened to be in the district on business, called on her at 51's house.
5353 informed her of her discovery and showed her the list she
had made. When her daughter pointed out that the list was not
accurate, 5353 asked her help to draw it up properly and this she
did. The difference in technical quality between the list of contents of 51's wallet and the descriptions written down in Achilles'
presence can consequently be explained by the help given by
5353's daughter to her mother.

2) It is correct that the door of 51's villa does not have a
safety-chain. It is fitted with a detachable *safety-bar*, about 5' 6"
long, which passes through two slots fixed on each side of the
door, thus preventing the door from opening. Since this detachable bar was kept in the kitchen during the day and the slots on
the wall were hidden by the curtains round the door, Menelaus
would have been unable to realize that they existed.

3) It is correct that 51 and 52 were invited to an official
reception at the Italian Embassy for the evening of 28.3.1968.
5353 was not informed that they were attending the reception

until the morning of the 27th. She immediately reported this fact to 5672 of her own accord.

Copy for information to Jupiter

Date: 11.4.1968
From: Mercury
To: Minerva
Subject: DL 51

Classification: TS
Ref. no. 2070 WA

Dead Leaves I

Geneviève de Maupertain, 52's sister, was born at Maupertain (Manche) on 15.12.1936, the daughter of Robert, born 8.6.1902 at Maupertain (Manche), farmer, and of Sabine Martin, born on 16.10.1915 at Quettehou (Manche), occupation housewife.

Secondary education, up to and including Grade 1 at the Lycée Jussieu in Cherbourg (Manche).

Secretary/Shorthand-Typist at the French Lawn Tennis Federation from 1955 to 1959.

Married Michel Dermoy on 1.2.1960.

Michel Dermoy, born on 9.4.1923 in Paris (XVI), son of Marcel, born on 8.6.1885 at Baslieux-lès-Fismes (Marnes), engineer with French Railways, and of Josépha Schneider, born on 18.11.1894 at Limoges (Haute-Vienne), occupation housewife, both deceased.

A younger brother Alain is at present curate in the parish of Notre-Dame des Prés (Paris VI).

Secondary education at the Lycée Louis-le-Grand in Paris.

Liaison agent in the Resistance Network 'Vanoise'. Arrested by the Gestapo on 27.12.1942 and deported to Mauthausen. Repatriated in 1945. Croix de Guerre 1939-1945 and Resistance Medal.

Married Georgie Cambernon, former Ravensbrück deportee, on 2.2.1946. One child, Hugues, born 7.9.1947. Georgie Cambernon died on 14.5.1948 from the effects of her experiences in Ravensbrück.

Called to the Paris Bar 1951.
Married Geneviève de Maupertain on 1.2.1960.
Two children.
    Robert, born on 9.3.1963 in Paris (VI)
    Jean-Louis, born on 18.9.1966 at Deauville (Calvados).

Maître Dermoy's chambers are situated at his home at 4 Rue Duret (Paris XVI). He specializes in international commercial law. Maître Dermoy looks after the interests of a number of large foreign concerns. He often travels for consultations to London and Brussels. He never undertakes criminal cases. He rarely appears at the Law Courts since his work consists mainly in bringing his clients' activities into line with the French legal system and with the new legal structures brought into being by the Common Market. His fees are high but difficult to assess precisely. They can certainly not amount to less than 150,000 francs p.a. net. He has a partner, Jacqueline Delamaison, 33 years old.

Dermoy belongs to no political party nor to any association of former resistance fighters or former deportees. He has not remained in touch with his former comrades in the 'Vanoise' network. He never wears his decorations.

He is not known to have a mistress.

He was formerly a tennis-player of rank, he gave up the sport three years ago after suspected heart-strain. He devotes all his spare time to playing bridge, in which he teams up with his wife. They play in a large number of tournaments.

Eighteen months ago he bought a share in the Lily International Club. This very smart club offers sporting and leisure facilities for its members in premises close to Chantilly. The Dermoys spend their weekends there when they are not away playing in bridge tournaments. In the summer they go to Trégastel where they have a large villa by the sea.

Hugues Dermoy, Michel's son by his first marriage, is a medical student at Paris University. He intends to become a chest surgeon. He is engaged to a medical student Marianne Varon. He was university champion for the Ile-de-France in the 800 metres in 1967.

Geneviève Dermoy, 52's sister, has followed no occupation

since her marriage. Thanks to her two full-time domestic servants, she has a great deal of spare time, which she spends playing bridge and taking part in advertising competitions. She has become something of a specialist in this sort of competition in which she has won numerous prizes. In 1965, in a competition organized by a Paris newspaper, she won the first prize of a trip round the world, which she took with her husband.

She was formerly junior tennis champion of Normandy but gave the game up at the same time as her husband.

In 1965 and 1966 she went on a winter-sports holiday with 51 and 52.

She is not known to have a lover.

Source: Demosthenes

Date: 12.4.1968   Classification: TS
From: Mercury   Ref. no. 2071 ZB
To: Minerva
Subject: Operation Zephyr

Further to the cancellation of Operation Zephyr, we note
Hecate's circular letter 8142 LA of today's date reporting the
arrival of the Persian Oribasis in Lagos (Nigeria).

Copy for information to Jupiter

Dead Leaves II

Preliminary investigations have enabled us to identify:

1) Marcelle Hamel, concierge at 31 Avenue de l'Observatoire,
   in which building 51 and 52 have their Paris home; Honoré
   Hamel, her husband, gardener employed by the Paris City
   Council
   Léonce d'Etchandart, widow, no occupation, tenant of the
   third-floor flat;
   Maurice Nauvois, engineer at the College of Arts and
   Crafts, tenant of the fourth-floor flat.

These four persons are mentioned in letter 1998 JP from 51 to
53 but do not seem to be closely connected with 51. Consequently,
subject to any counter-instructions from you, we do not propose
to subject them to closer scrutiny.

2) Michel and Annie Roldoire, 12 Boulevard des Sablons,
   Neuilly. Michel Roldoire is Sales Director of the firm
   'United Paris Textiles'. His wife has no occupation. Two
   children;
   Henri Allix M.D., 54 Rue du Bac, Paris (VII), died in
   March 1967;
   Antoinette Lieuvert, retired Civil Servant, 8 rue Delambre,
   Paris (XIV), owner of the property at 31 Avenue de
   l'Observatoire.

These four persons are mentioned in the list of contents of 51's
wallet (ref. 1999 HN). The relationship between Antoinette
Lieuvert and her tenant 51 does not, subject to any counter-

172

instructions from you, seem to warrant further scrutiny. Investigation of Michel and Annie Roldoire will continue.

3) Jacques Le Noir M.D., paediatrician, 89 Rue de Rennes, Paris (VI), 43 years old, married with six children.

Mentioned in the letter 2038 MM from 52 to 51. Dr Le Noir's connection with 51 seems purely professional and, subject to counter-instructions from you, we do not propose to subject him to any closer scrutiny.

1) 55 returned to Paris on 13.4.1968. She is living with her contact 8956.

2) 5353's daughter is replacing her in 51's house.

3) Further to the cancellation of Operation Zephyr, we beg to report that, on interrogation by 8956, 55 stated that 51 closeted himself in his office every Thursday evening on urgent work that had to be completed by Friday afternoon.

Date: 18.4.1968   Classification: TS
From: Minerva   Ref. no. 2074 KG
To: Mercury
Subject: 51

5353's daughter will be allotted the identification number 5354.

Copy for information to Hecate

Date: 18.4.1968
From: Mercury
To: Minerva
Subject: DL 51

Classification: TS
Ref. no. 2075 EP

Dead Leaves III

Investigations have been pursued to discover persons having had contact with 51 at the institutions and units mentioned in the records file, viz:

1) Ecole Saint-Patrice, 8 Rue Cassette (Paris, VI)
2) Collège Ladislas, 19 Rue de Fleurus (Paris, VI)
3) 24th I.T.R.
4) O.T.R. Cherchell
5) 117th I.R.

1) The Ecole Saint-Patrice no longer exists. It did not prove possible to obtain access to its list of old boys.

2) 8047 called on the Old Boys' Association of the Collège Ladislas, posing as the chief publicity agent for a property company constructing holiday flats and villas on the Côte d'Azur. He succeeded in obtaining the list of members by agreeing to pay for the next three editions of the Old Boys' Bulletin. We made a sample selection of 13 persons from amongst 51's 284 fellow-pupils during the course of his seven years at the school. 8653 approached the 13 selected persons by telephone representing himself to be the Secretary of the Collège Ladislas Old Boys' Association. These telephonic enquiries produced the following results:

a) 4 had no recollection of 51;

b) 6 remembered that they had been in the same class as 51 but could remember nothing else about him;

c) Larrifol Etienne, an actor residing at 42 Rue de la Huchette,

176

Paris (V), a fellow-pupil of 51 in Grade 4 (1944-1945), described 51 as a rather reserved and not very pleasant boy who was liked by the masters. 51 belonged to the J.E.C. group (Jeunesse Etudiante Chrétienne) at Ladislas.

d) Valenberg Martial, chartered accountant, residing at 19 Rue des Hauts, Marseilles (Bouches-du-Rhône), 51's fellow-pupil in Grade 3 (1945-1946), stated that 51 was a shy boy and difficult to know. As a day-boy, he took little part in the life of the school. He was very good indeed at French and very bad at science and mathematics. At that time, 51 used to say that he wanted to be a writer or a pilot. He belonged to a scout troop outside the school.

e) Janin Sébastien, company director, residing at 105 Avenue Victor Hugo, Paris (XVI), 51's fellow-pupil in Grade 1 (Philosophy) (1948-1949), told 8653 that 51 had been suspended for a week because he had taken a pornographic book to school.

A further sample of 13 persons has been selected. As a security precaution we shall make no further enquiries for three months.

3) The only means of approaching former members of the three units in which 51 completed his national service is via the National Association of Reserve Officers and the Union Nationale d'Anciens Combattants d'Algérie. No action was taken since these organizations come under the terms of Hecate's 4801 ZZ of 23.7.1964 (banned organizations).

Date: 18.4.1968   Classification: TS
From: Venus   Ref. no. 2076 MA
To: Minerva
Subject: Operation Jumping

Our agent Paris reports first contact with target satisfactorily
accomplished on 11.4.1968.

Date: 22.4.1968
From: Mercury
To: Minerva
Subject: DL 51

Classification: TS
Ref. no. 2077 VC

Dead Leaves IV

Monique de Servas, married name Auphal, 51's mother, was born on 12.12.1905 at Bourges (Cher), daughter of Joachim, born 29.1.1867 at Levet (Cher), and of Mélanie Toudroit, born on 17.11.1874 at Saint-Etienne (Loire).

One brother, Gaston, born 14.2.1898, killed at Saint-Mihiel on 14.8.1917.

Joachim de Servas, 51's grandfather, farmer at Levet (Cher), married at the age of 29 Mélanie Toudroit, daughter of Alphonse Toudroit, ironmaster, at Vierzon (Cher). He gave up farming to work with his father-in-law, whom he succeeded in 1904. His business seems to have gone rapidly downhill and he had to return to farming just before the First World War. He died in 1929. His wife Mélanie Toudroit died in 1938.

Their daughter Monique, 51's mother, was educated at the Dominican convent in Bourges and took her 'baccalauréat'.

She worked for a 'licence' in Arts at the Institut Catholique in Paris.

She married Lucien Auphal on 1.10.1925.

Lucien Auphal, born 15.8.1890 in Bordeaux (Gironde), son of James, born in Pointe-à-Pitre (Guadeloupe) on 19.10.1865, and of Emilienne Butard, born at Morcenx (Landes) on 27.7.1869, both deceased.

Five brothers:

Henri, born on 17.2.1893, killed at Verdun on 21.7.1916
Pierre, born on 1.9.1895, killed at Verdun on 17.8.1916

Louis, born on 24.4.1898, killed at Chemin-des-Dames on
10.2.1918

Gabriel, born on 1.12.1902, died on 6.2.1934

Laurent, born on 12.6.1905

Secondary education at the Lycée of Bordeaux.

Medical Studies at the University of Bordeaux.

Called up in 1915. Wounded on the Somme (Croix de Guerre).
Promoted lieutenant. Wounded in 1916 in Flanders (Legion of
Honour). Promoted captain in 1917 and major in 1918.

G.P. at Langdon (Gironde) from 1920 to 1926.

Settled in Paris in 1926.

Died on 13.2.1961.

Two children:

Lucie, born on 9.12.1926 in Paris, died 18.7.1927;

51.

Monique de Servas, widow of Lucien Auphal, now aged sixty-
three, still lives at 82 Rue Guynemer (Paris VI) where 51 was
born. She occupies a five-room flat on the second floor. She lives
modestly. She spends four afternoons a week on charity work
for the International Association of Former Resistance Deportees. She is highly regarded amongst her neighbours, who
describe her as a quiet sort of person, but always ready to help
people.

Source and remarks:

Information gathered by 8016 who called on the subject under
the pretext of making enquiries on behalf of the Ministry for
Ex-Servicemen.

8016 reports that the subject intends to go and stay with 51 and
52 from 27.4.1968 to 3.5.1968. He suggests that the flat be
searched in her absence.

Date: 22.4.1968   Classification: TS
From: Minerva   Ref. no. 2078 TK
To: Mars
Subject: Operation Lindbergh

Please provide a search specialist to undertake a house inspection
W/T at 82 Rue Guynemer, Paris. He is to place himself under
Mercury's orders. Mercury will provide all necessary routine
details.

The operation will be undertaken between 27.4.1968 and
3.5.1968 and has been allotted the code-name Lindbergh.

Copy for information to Mercury

Date: 23.4.1968
From: Mrcuery
To: Minerva
Subject: DL 51

Classification: TS
Ref. no. 2079 WB

Dead Leaves V

1) From information provided by 55, it has proved possible to identify:

Bérasse, Hervé, journalist, living at 116 Boulevard Flandrin, Paris (XVI), mentioned in a letter 1994 ZA from 51 to 52. Bérasse is aged about thirty-five and knew 52 before his marriage. 55 does not exclude the possibility of sexual intercourse between them before and/or after the marriage. Bérasse's visits have become far less frequent after he failed to pay back by the agreed date a loan which 51 had made to him.

Derelle, Simone, company secretary, living at 18 Rue du Cardinal-Lemoine, Paris (V), mentioned in the letter of the above ref. Simone Derelle is about forty years old. 55 describes her as 'fat, ugly, dirty, smelly and boring' (extract from recording by 8956). She has never heard 51 and 52 say a good word about her, and cannot understand why they kept on inviting her.

Brauchit, Jean-François, sales representative, living at 89 Rue Guillaume, Flers (Orne), mentioned in the list of contents of 51's wallet (ref. 1999 HN). According to 55, Brauchite, about thirty years old, was an officer in 51's old regiment. He used to telephone when he was in Paris in order to get himself invited by 51. This irritated 52.

Guivon, Thérèse, occupation housewife, wife of Guivon, Daniel, civil servant in the Ministry of Finance, living at 236 Boulevard Murat, Paris (XVI), mentioned in letter 2038 MM from 52 to 51. According to 55, Thérèse Guivon, aged about thirty, is a social acquaintance of 52's. She used to come to tea occasionally.

Investigations on these four persons are being pursued further.

2) 55 was unable to provide any help towards identifying:

Jacky X (Letter 2038 MM from 52 to 51)

Delattre (ditto)

M. and Mme Durand (ditto)

3) Three persons were described by 55 as being particularly close to 51 and/or 52:

Dermoy, Alain, younger brother of Maître Dermoy (v. DL 1, ref. 2070 WA). As curate of the parish of Notre-Dame des Prés, which is situated close to the Avenue de l'Observatoire, he used to drop in often for lunch or dinner. Aged about forty. 55 was particularly struck by the way he dressed (rolled-neck sweater, black leather tunic) and by his extreme views (extract from 8956's recording: 'he used to talk like a proper commie').

Dermoy, Geneviève, 52's sister, sister-in-law of the previous person (v. DL I, ref. 2070 WA). Geneviève Dermoy and 52 are very fond of each other. They used to spend several afternoons a week together, going shopping or going to the cinema. Although Geneviève Dermoy is slightly older than 52, it is the latter, according to 55, who acts the part of the elder sister.

Champon, Isaure, living at 180, rue Marx Dormoy, Paris (XVIII). Aged about thirty, she is said to be a childhood friend of 52. She used to come to lunch at the Avenue de l'Observatoire fairly often, but in 51's absence, because her tendency to drink too much irritated him. 55 saw her a number of times in the company of coloured men.

Investigation of Alain Dermoy and Isaure Champon is continuing.

4) 55 mentioned the names of a number of 51's professional associates who, as such, fall outside the terms of reference of DL 51 (v. your memo 2063 DM, para. 6, of 27.3.1968).

5) 55 provides some information as to 51's and 52's marital relations. It would seem that these relations are characterized by a certain coldness. 55 states that she has never seen them kiss each other. She has never heard 51 compliment 52 on her

physical appearance or her clothes. According to her, their sexual relations are extremely restricted, if not non-existent. 51 gives 52 a very free hand in the house and in her house-keeping expenses. 55 has never seen them quarrel or discuss money matters. According to her, disagreement between them is very rare and they seem rather to be living together like two strangers. Questioned as to the reasons for such an attitude, 55 replied that 'they must have a skeleton in their cupboard and they want to keep it shut in all the time rather than talk about it' (extract from 8956's recording). According to her, the staff at Maupertain (52's parents' estate) thought that 54 was not 51's daughter and this was the reason for 51's coldness towards his wife and for his special affection for 53. 55 admitted however that she could not give any precise evidence to support this statement. She added: 'In our parts, a man can't have a son without people gossiping all over the place and saying that the father's the postman or the gamekeeper, and you're lucky if they don't blame the priest for it.' (Extract from 8956's recording.)

6) According to 55, 52 enjoys excellent health. 51 is always complaining of having sick-headaches. He says he suffers from shortness of breath caused by nerves and that he has a feeling of suffocating. He only drinks mineral water and has a poor appetite. He is always worrying about his health and keeps thinking he has cancer. He takes several pills before every meal. According to 55, 52 does not take 51's anxieties seriously and the doctors consider them unfounded.

Remarks:

8956 reports that 55 is showing increasing reluctance to talk about her former employers. She is very concerned about the reaction of her parents when they learn about her leaving Delphi. 8956 considers that it will soon become impossible for him to continue to be evasive with regard to 55's ever-increasing pressure to get him to fix the date of their wedding. Failing a decision in the near future, 55 might decide to go back to Delphi, which would involve the risk of her telling 51 and 52 about her affair, and the special interest that her 'fiancé' had shown concerning them. We request instructions.

184

Enclosures:

8956's tape-recordings containing 18 hrs 22 mins playing-time, most of them offering no interest. Extracts have been quoted in the above report, which is based on the information obtained from them.

Dead Leaves VI

Robert de Maupertain, 52's father, was born on 8.6.1902 at Maupertain (Manche), son of Frédéric, born on 4.8.1882 at Cherbourg (Manche) and of Agnès Labrit, born on 31.10.1884 at Valognes (Manche).

On the outbreak of the Second World War, Robert de Maupertain was mobilized in a tank regiment. He was wounded during the Montcorndet counter-offensive. He was taken prisoner and sent to the Stalag at Hildesheim. First attempt to escape on 17.9.1940. Second attempt on 24.12.1940. Transferred to the fortress at Schweinfurt. Succeeded in escaping on 5.5.1941. Arrested at the Franco-Spanish frontier on 19.8.1941. Condemned to death by the German Military Tribunal of Bordeaux. Escaped whilst being transferred to Germany on 10.4.1942. Section leader in the F.T.P. (Francs-Tireurs Partisans) in the Limousin. Wounded on 12.6.1943. Company commander during the operations in the spring of 1944. Promoted colonel after the liberation of Limoges. Incorporated into the First French Army with the rank of captain. Finished the war in that unit. Decorations: Legion of Honour, Croix de Guerre with bar, Escaped Prisoners' Medal, Resistance Medal.

Robert de Maupertain has remained in touch with some of his former comrades in the Limousin maquis, most of them communists. He still continues to invite them, with their families, to his manor-house during the summer holidays. He sent back all his decorations to the Head of State after the First Foreign Regiment of the French Foreign Legion, in which he served from

1924 to 1930, was dissolved in 1961. His political activity is confined to a token subscription to the Free Brittany movement.

On his return to Maupertain, he took over the management of the family estate which had been run in his absence by his mother and his wife (it is worth noting that since his return he has never taken the trouble to see his brothers-in-law and his sister-in-law, whom he blames for having sided with Vichy).

Although not as prosperous as his family used to be, it can be said that he is comfortably off.

He is generally well-liked in the district of Saint-Pierre-Eglise, despite his impulsiveness and quick temper. His obstinacy and his red hair have earned him the nickname of the 'Red Mule'.

His wife, now aged fifty-three, is a self-effacing woman completely under her husband's thumb. According to unverified gossip, in 1942 she became incapable of child-bearing as the result of an operation but did not dare tell her husband, who wanted a male child to continue the Maupertain line. According to this same gossip, on Robert de Maupertain's return, an extra place was always laid at family meals, to mark the place for 'our son'. This practice was said to have lasted for several years, until Robert's mother undertook to inform him of her daughter-in-law's operation.

He seems to have mixed feelings for 51 and is reluctant to mention him. His relationship with his other son-in-law, Maître Dermoy, is much more cordial, as a result of their both having belonged to the Resistance. He disapproves of the way 53 and 54 are being brought up 'in cotton wool'. He contrasts it with the energetic, 'sporty' upbringing that Maître Dermoy gave his elder son.

According to 55, 51's and 52's engagement was nearly broken off as the result of a sudden emergency. 52 unexpectedly came back to Maupertain a week or two before the marriage and had a number of stormy sessions with her father. A visit from 51's mother succeeded in putting matters right. Robert de Maupertain is said to have been refusing to pay the dowry he had promised. According to the servants, this refusal was motivated at least as much by his financial difficulties as by his grievance against 51, the nature of which is not known.

According to 55, he is not known to have had any affairs since his return in 1945, whereas before the war they were said to have been numerous. He has a certain liking for alcohol.

Sources:
  55
  8047, who contacted the subject under the cover of being the owner of a Paris riding club, as well as a number of other breeders in the district, under the same cover.

Date: 26.4.1968
From: Mercury
To: Minerva
Subject: 5354

Classification: TS
Ref. no. 2081 CP

5354 has reported the following facts to her contact 5672:

1) 51 and 52 have been greatly put out by 55's departure, which was quite unexpected. They could not prevent it because 55 had just come of age. They have written to 55's parents to warn them that 55 has left, in order to relieve themselves of any further responsibility for her.

2) 52 is satisfied with 5354's work but the two children look on her as an intruder who was responsible for 55's departure. They were very fond of 55. Their hostility thus greatly hampers 5354's activity since she is spied on all the time by the children, who report everything she does to 52, in the hope of getting her dismissed.

3) 5354 describes the family life as harmonious and seemingly very happy. According to her, 51 and 52 get on very well. She emphasizes how faithful 51 is to his wife. Her first impression of 52 was that she was interested in other men but she (5354) is less sure now. According to her, 52 has been telling 51 about a man who is making up to her at the riding-school where she goes three mornings a week. 52 and 51 joke together about this man who is said to be very tall and strong, with thick eyebrows and a threatening look. They call him King Kong. According to 5354, 52 receives letters from no one but her sister or her parents. She seems to be very happy in Delphi, and is talking of buying a horse to take part in jumping competitions.

4) 5672 has asked for permission to indulge in sexual intercourse with 5354, as unless he does, it will be difficult to remain

189

her contact. As an exception to routine regulations, in view of 5354's peculiar characteristics, we consider it appropriate to grant this permission, subject to any contrary decision from you.

Date: 26.4.1968   Classification: TS
From: Minerva   Ref. no. 2082 KZ
To: Venus
Subject: Operation Jumping

Operation cancelled. Recall Paris. We asked you for a Rhett
Butler, not an orang-outang.

Date: 28.4.1968
From: Mercury
To: Minerva
Subject: DL 51

Classification: TS
Ref. no. 2083 DC

Dead Leaves VII

A visiting card bearing the name: 'M. and Mme Roldoire, 12 Boulevard des Sablons, 92, Neuilly-sur-Seine, 722 18-44' appears on the list of contents of 51's wallet (ref. 1999 HN).

Preliminary enquiries enabled us to identify Michel Roldoire, Sales Director of the firm of 'United Paris Textiles' and his wife Annie, occupation housewife, two children (v. DL II, ref. 2072 QP).

According to information obtained by 8248 (posing as a welfare officer) Michael Roldoire, aged forty-three, was until 1967 manager of the Moroccan branch in Rabat of the firm of which he is now the Sales Manager. He could thus have met 51 and 52 in Rabat.

Following this enquiry, 8653 rang up Annie Roldoire posing as a friend of 52 who had been asked by the latter to inform Mme Roldoire of her departure for Delphi and to give her her new address. Mme Roldoire seemed surprised at this concern on 52's part. She replied, 'What a pity, we were always hoping to see each other again and we didn't get round to it, and now it looks as if we shan't be seeing each other for some time.'

Questioned by 8956, 55 also made it clear that she had never seen the Roldoires at 51's and 52's house and that she had never heard them mention their name.

It would seem, in consequence, that the relationship between the Roldoires and 51 is not worth further investigation.

Date: 2.5.1968   Classification: TS
From: Mercury   Ref. no. 2084 BZ
To: Minerva
Subject: DL 51

Dead Leaves VIII

Operation Lindbergh was carried out on the afternoon of 27.4.1968 by 8848 accompanied by 2429, lent by Mars.

8848's report shows that the flat occupied by the subject is a typical French middle-class flat in its lay-out, furniture and decoration.

He draws attention, however, to two peculiarities:

1) The bedroom door was locked. 2429 took the lock to pieces during 8848's search. His examination of it led him to conclude that the door had not merely been locked on this occasion, in connection with the tenant's absence, but that the state of the spring proves that the door remains locked for most of the time.

The tenant's bedroom was untidy and very dirty. There were numerous bottles of whisky, full and empty, lying on the floor. The furniture was littered with large numbers of glasses. The bed was unmade. The sheets were stained and full of holes burnt by cigarettes. There was a heap of dirty underwear in a corner.

There were four photos of 51 at different ages on various pieces of furniture. A large photo showing piles of naked emaciated corpses, with barrack-huts in the background, was pinned on the wall opposite the bed. According to 8848, it could be a photo of a liberated German deportee camp.

2) The bedroom formerly occupied by 51 was tidy and kept dusted. The bed was made up.

A large map of the world covered part of a wall. Above the map was fixed a strip of paper on which was written by hand in capitals: MY COUNTRY MUST BE THE GREATEST IN

THE WORLD. To judge by the faded ink, this inscription has been there for some considerable time.

The wall-cupboard and wardrobe were full of used clothing.

In the subject's bedroom, 8848 discovered and examined a great number of various papers (letters, bills, printed matter) of no particular interest except for an envelope with the following inscription written by hand: 'For Dominique when I have passed on'.

Inside the envelope were three documents which were photographed by 8848 and replaced in the envelope, viz:

Letter from the subject to 51 (Appendix I)

Letter from Valérie Rossignat to 51 (Appendix II)

Letter from the subject to 51 pinned to the previous letter (Appendix IIA).

The absence of any other personal documents in the subject's bedroom can probably be explained by the existence of the safe mentioned in Appendix I. It is a Starway 1936 model built into the wall of a room which must have been the study of the subject's husband. It is hidden behind a picture. 2429 came to the conclusion after examining it that it would be possible to open it but that it would leave traces. He therefore refrained in view of the instructions that he had received to carry out a search W/T.

In 51's bedroom, 8848 discovered and examined a certain number of papers and various objects contained in a small carved wooden box, padlocked and placed on top of the wardrobe. He made a list of the contents, which is enclosed with photocopies as follows:

Various objects, descriptive list (Appendix III)

Various documents, descriptive list (Appendix IV)

Undated handwritten documents (Appendix V)

Letters addressed to 51 (Appendix VI).

Enclosures: Appendices I to VI

Appendix I

Paris, Easter Monday 1962

My darling boy,

I think that it must be something that Marguerite Cadera said which has made me take my pen and write to you on this Easter Monday in a Paris which is so deserted as to be unrecognizable. After the funeral, while I was kissing Marguerite, who was in tears, she said to me: 'If only it hadn't happened so quickly, if only we could have had just one hour together first, there were so many things I wanted to say to him!' At that moment the thought came to me that the dead follow the dead, one after the other, and each one is different because, throughout the whole time your father was dying, he didn't once break the silence that stood between us. Was it because we had nothing more to say to each other, or because there would have been too much to say? I can't tell. And then I thought of you, so far away at the moment but who will be coming back to me one day to kiss my lips which will never open again to answer all your questions. My darling Dominique, my dear, dear son, how many hours we have spent talking to each other since those happy days when you used to come and snuggle up to me in bed as soon as you were awake, up to the time when during your final years as a student you would invite me so ceremoniously to come to tea in your room? I think that rarely can any other mother and son have known that heartfelt communion, that mysterious understanding that meant that I could feel all your secret joys even when you pretended to

195

be bored and that you knew my hidden sorrow even when life's demands made me pretend to be unemotional. And yet how many barriers there are still between us and how many mysteries that you can't explain, the key to which I shall take with me to the grave! One can know one's own child – or can think one does – but who can know what his mother is like, even when she is the most beloved of mothers and the most loving? Your problems, or what you called your problems – and sometimes they were – we were able to share together, and some of them we were able to solve together. But mine had to remain locked up in my heart. You will realize when Steve and Lolo are bigger that a child is like a frail little boat that you watch with an anxious heart sailing towards the open sea loaded with so many heavy stones that it is right down to the water-line, so that it is impossible to overload it any more with one's own cargo of fears and failures. Ah, Dominique, I was wrecked long ago ... Did you ever realize that? I think not and I earnestly hope not. At least I was successful in hiding that.

Yet four years ago I was on the point of telling you when I saw you so unhappy and helpless and at a loss at the violence of your father's attitude. But I pulled myself together. As usual, your father was wrong in the way he was behaving, but on this occasion what he was doing was right. I'm sure that now you are quite clear about that. But unfortunately the good reasons that he was giving you became bad ones in your eyes merely because they were coming from him and the lack of understanding that he had always shown towards you made you feel that even now he was merely trying to dominate and bully you. Ah Dominique, how I wanted to cry out to you: 'It's true he doesn't love you, it's true he's always been horrible to you, but this time you must listen to him because what he's saying is right!'

And I was tempted to speak out again a year ago. Do you remember the long vigil we kept together. In death he seemed less remote than when he was alive. At last his eyelids were hiding that look that used to terrify us ... Yes, he used to terrify me too. The frightful, grotesque sounds that were coming from his body seemed to make him vulnerable and human at last. You could feel sorry for him. I was pretending to pray and you were talking under your breath. You talked to him all night, just as if

I hadn't been there, as if you were asking him, now he was dead, to explain things that you hadn't dared to ask him when he was alive, and which he certainly would never have told you. I was counting my beads without thinking while I listened to what you were saying, and I was praying, not for him but for myself – that I might be granted strength to stay silent while my son was asking why his childhood had been so unhappy.

And then there was that remark of Marguerite's: Nicholas was exactly my age. For some time now, the Figaro has been mercilessly killing off my contemporaries in its obituary columns. We must accept the fact that we're not immortal. Have *you* ever realized, really understood, that you're going to die one day? It struck me like a thunderbolt on my thirtieth birthday. For six whole months I went about haunted by the idea of death. In those days they hadn't started talking about nervous depression. And then, slowly, I got used to the idea. You can get used to anything, as you'll see. Marguerite didn't make me terrified again, she merely reminded me to set my house in order.

I shall take with me all sorts of things that have no interest for anyone any longer, but those things were, in fact, my life. When I was thirty and heard death knocking at my door all the time, what appalled me was that it would be robbing me of my future. And now it's the thought of the past that it will destroy for ever that fills me with dismay. When I die, my mother, my father and my brother will die a second time with me and not one living person will know how they looked. When I die, the whole of the Servas family will be in the grave. Well, there's nothing to be done and I know my Barres well enough for that. And incidentally, you'll see that it's the times that were lightest that will weigh heaviest in the final balance. My father's suffering on his death-bed – he died quickly but in dreadful agony – that may well disappear when I do, but what a pity that our rides round the estate will vanish at the same time; I was sixteen, and we would canter in the mist, through the dawn, and the rabbits scuttled away under the horses' hooves. When we left we were shivering, and when we came back we were soaked in perspiration and the spot where we changed from being cold to hot was at old Jeanne's place where we used to drink rum. Mama rubbed me down whilst I took my boots off and I didn't answer her

197

questions so that she wouldn't smell the rum. I don't think she ever knew. Sometimes Papa would even make me chew some coffee beans. Your grandfather was a disastrous man. He ran through his wife's dowry, ruined his wife's parents, and borrowed money from all his friends without ever paying them back. He deceived Mother all the time, and I know that I've got several highly natural brothers and sisters at Levet (go back there one day: you'll see that the Servas nose is very popular). Dozens of times he was on the point of doing some work but he never actually started any. He used to say that our early morning rides were his work, as if the master's eye cast over the estate was enough to make the oats and corn grow. His sister, Aunt Martha, used to explain that he was a selfish monster. His brother, Uncle Ferdinand, used to grumble that he was a good-for-nothing. And I adored him, rather guiltily, like a good girl who's fond of a bad lad. What's more, everyone liked him. He ruined us all with the greatest good humour in the world. Under his light-hearted guidance, we went from one disaster to the next as cheerfully as could be. I think he had every fault, except conventional middle-class ones. After his death, at the age when girls begin to be a bit stupid (in my day it coincided with reading Henry Bordeaux), I made a sort of agonizing reappraisal of him, as I think you put it. He had been, and always would be, a marvellous father, but as an unfaithful, lazy husband he must certainly have made Mama very unhappy. During the last few days of your grandmother's life (poor Dominique! Nicholas, your father, your grandfather, your grandmother – what a lot of death-bed scenes there are in this letter which, what is more, you'll be reading at my death-bed! You must bear up. Remember the story of the good man who bears witness), a few days before she passed away, then, I raised the subject of the trials and tribulations of being married to my father, and with what I thought was perfect tact, I half hinted that her life hadn't been very happy and that it might even have been a hell on earth. She looked at me for a long time and I could see that she wanted to explain something, and then her face suddenly lit up and she looked incredibly young as she said: 'You know, with your father I was never bored.' She even gave me a wink which was quite out of character.

She was a saint and a marvellous mother, but she still managed

198

to be a disaster for me just as surely as my father, with all his shortcomings, had given me the happiest childhood possible. Your grandfather was broadminded, or perhaps he had no mind at all, if you like. He allowed me to continue my education after leaving school which was very unusual for a girl at that time and in our class of society. Thanks to him, I'd been able to go and study at the Institut Catholique in Paris. It's true that the Catholic student hostel where I was living bore no resemblance to the bohemian sort of life in the Latin Quarter, but it was bold enough to horrify the nuns at Bourges, and they prophesied that I would be coming back one day, horresco referens, with a cigarette in my mouth and even with short hair! I wanted to go on for a diploma and become a teacher. Marriage? No hurry for that. I didn't even think about it. But now that she was widowed and left on her own, Mama soon made me think of it. Daddy's sudden death had in a way deprived her of her guiding light. Nothing had prepared her for it. Three hours before he took to his bed he had been riding round the estate on Querpro. He had left his affairs in a dreadful state for Mama. She found that she was ruined. His papers showed that Papa owed large sums to old friends who had kept on accepting invitations to the house without being tactless enough to mention money. She felt that she was disgraced. Wise Maître Novet was given the task of trying to tidy things up. As for her, she set about putting me on the straight and narrow. One year later, I woke up to find myself married. It was a subtle attack and I surrendered ingloriously. Papa hadn't left me a penny: he hadn't a penny to leave. Mama had just inherited from her sister Louise. My university studies were paid for by her. The question of money was not mentioned of course. In our family, we're wonderful at hinting at things without ever mentioning them.

It was the sort of marriage that you won't find any more. Thanks to Aunt Louise, I had a dowry. Your father had been practising for five or six years near Bordeaux. He wanted to set up in Paris, which required money, and to settle there, which meant having a wife. Our Cupid was Maître Novet. It was in his drawing-room that I saw your father for the first time. Do you remember how we used to be reduced to helpless laughter whenever we used to read the marriage advertisements? But I was

199

really laughing on the wrong side of my face. I was thinking that it was in fact rather more fun to meet at 'Le Chasseur Français' than at Maître Novet's. But after all, your father had good table manners, he had read Verlaine, he was a doctor, he had a fine war record, which meant something in those days, and what is more, he was tall: you know, thanks to reading 'Le Chasseur Français', that that is an important detail for a woman. So why not marry him?

You know, with your father I was always bored. There's no point in talking about his strictness, his puritanism, the hard cold way he looked at everything and everyone. But in all fairness there were reasons for all this. Let me tell you a few of them at least. They were very simple. You have to realize that the men of that generation were the survivors of a holocaust. Nowadays cars go too fast to let you read on the War Memorials of even the tiniest village the terrible list of names of all those who failed to come back in 1918. Louis, the one who looked so much like your father, has his name on the one at Levet. There are the names of three Auphals in Bordeaux. Just think of it: three! Your father was haunted by the memory of his brothers. In a certain sense, the euphoria that followed the victory justified the slaughter: the dead had not died in vain, it was thanks to them that we had won. But then followed a period of general confusion everywhere, the decline of France, political scandals. So what was the gain? Had the three Auphal brothers merely died to make the world safe for corruption and filthy lucre? Had your father been twice wounded just for nothing? Everything seemed to suggest so but he wouldn't accept it. And so he withdrew into his shell and became first of all pessimistic and then contemptuous of other people, a contempt that quickly turned to hate. He reacted by shutting himself up in an ivory tower, quite unlike his brother Gabriel, who was twelve years younger and hadn't been to the war. Ah my darling Dominique, when you used to become so irritated at the 'taboo on Gabriel' I sometimes asked myself if you really were quite so bright, although you gave every proof of it. Knowing that he had died on February 6th 1934, didn't you ever connect it with a certain political event? Well, that's what it was – your Uncle Gabriel was killed by the garde mobile in the Place de la Concorde. He was taking part in a Croix-de-Feux demonstration. He had decided to play an active role in politics. And all because of his three dead brothers. You see, for the Auphals the war didn't end in 1918. And it was the First World War, too, that your uncle Laurent, the youngest of the five, thought he was still fighting when he joined the Militia in 1944. Today he's living in the Argentine and they say he's become an important person in industry there. That explains the 'taboo about Laurent' as well.

One year after our marriage, Lucie was born. She was taken from us only seven months later. My grief was so immense that I thought I could never be consoled. Yet time did its work, and above all a thought, the rather dreadful thought: should I have been able to love in her the part that came from him. Go on reading and you'll understand. Poor Lucie. After she had gone, we were going to live amongst the dead, surrounded, shut in by them. I saw your father cut off one after the other all the contacts which linked him to the world, except his professional ones. I'd given up my studies. I'd stopped reading. We never went out. Our few friends became tired of your father's gloominess and my sadness. It was like a sort of incurable paralysis that gets worse and worse. We didn't love each other. We had never loved each other. All the same we had to manage to live together. I cut myself down to size. I shrank. I made myself as small as I could but it was still not small enough for your father. He wanted me to be like him, that is to say dead, and he knew that I was only pretending. When someone's been buried alive, they're bound to knock on the lid of the coffin. In 1928 I ran away for the first time and went home to my mother. I was at the end of my tether. I was suffocating. She soon brought me back to the fold. In 1930, in June I remember, I escaped for ever but without leaving the matrimonial home. I had met a man. Your father. Your real father.

Dominique darling, I beg you to forgive me the sorrow I'm causing you. I'd have been so much happier if I could have tip-toed away without saying a word. But it would be too cowardly. As it was, I used to feel ashamed of myself when I heard you saying how sorry you were for my wasted life. And I shook my head hypocritically whereas I should have cried out to you that my life had contained eleven years of happiness. I didn't even give you a wink . . .

And anyway, I'm no longer concerned, I'm going to be called to other things or else to nothing at all, that's as may be. But for the night when we watched over my husband – I shall call him that from now on – I should have kept silent. It seemed to me that all your sorrows had died down, that the stream of life, your wife, your children, your career had washed away those early years. But that long vigil taught me differently. A life is like a tree: it all depends on the roots, that is on childhood. Yours was poisoned by the aversion my husband felt towards you. I tried to make up for it by giving you more of my love, but too much weight on one side of the balance only increased the difference, and how could any child understand what is inexplicable or accept what is unacceptable – the fact that his father doesn't love him? As a youth and even as a young man you were crippled by it, and even now, as an adult, you bear the scars. How I wish that this letter may bring you peace at last!

I know I have left it late. I know that I ought to have told you before. You must forgive me for being cowardly. I was afraid of what you would do. I was terrified that it would break up everything between us – and you are all I have left. I trembled at the thought that you might take his side. You had always been so open-hearted towards him despite his ill-treatment. You were scandalized by the way he treated me but you seemed to find his harshness towards you something quite normal, however unfair it was and however much it made you suffer. For him, you always pleaded guilty. Oh how often I've lain awake at night endlessly haunted by that terrible remark that Dr Allix once made: 'Children always know, even if they don't know that they know.' During that long vigil, when he had lost his domineering airs, all his powers to condemn, you didn't accuse him, you were questioning him, still looking for an explanation so that you might understand him and perhaps forgive him. If I had given you that explanation, as I was tempted to, wouldn't you have cried out that I was responsible for everything? And what could I have answered? That I had the same right to live and love as anyone else? One can't say that to one's child, one can hardly write it, or else only in a letter like this, and even then one can't be sure of being understood. And besides, what son wouldn't condemn his mother to suffer the torments of Tantalus? Perhaps you're going

202

to side with him, you may even have already done so, but at least I shall have held on to your love until my dying day.

As for the rest, don't worry, I've paid and paid bitterly. My husband was ruthless. He knew all about it very soon: I was never very subtle. And in any case we loved each other so dearly that we didn't even think of hiding ourselves. His only reaction was to batten everything down still more closely. He was like a blank wall. He refused to divorce me. His contempt for me was so great that I didn't seem worth all the trouble of taking me to court. He plunged late into his work and used his home only as a hotel. He was completely indifferent when you were born. He never complained at your crying, he never asked how you were. It was as if you didn't exist. I thought I should go mad. That lasted three years. After that he had to start replying, even if only yes or no, to the stream of questions that you never stopped asking us. We reached a rough sort of understanding. He tolerated your existence while still denying its origin. It was only a truce and many times it was broken, too. The war was bound to start up again as soon as you reached the age when a child begins to raise problems.

It all came to a head during the year you were eleven. There was your operation; you had difficulties at school; you ran away. He was forced to look after you and even take trouble over you: after all, he was your father in the eyes of the law. Was it then that his indifference towards me turned into a sort of furious rage, which could only be satisfied in acts? I don't know. I never understood what had happened to him. He had never seemed to look on my unfaithfulness as being anything more than a proof of how unworthy I was, and he seemed to take the same sort of disgruntled pleasure in it that he felt for everything. Sometimes I even had the feeling that your presence gave him a kind of satisfaction: you were living proof that the world consisted of mediocrity, lies and vice. I would ask myself at times if he wasn't sick in mind and as anxious to destroy himself as other people. There were the three Auphals killed in the trenches, and another one lying dead in a Paris street, of course, but now we were in the middle of another war and there were new piles of corpses covering the old graves. There's another possibility that sometimes gave me a sudden pang in my heart. I always refused to think about it but I'll confess it to you because I want to tell you everything. Perhaps, in his way, he loved me, perhaps he was jealous of me, perhaps he wasn't sick in mind but sick at heart and unable to communicate just as someone sick in body is unable to walk? Or else he was just moved by political motives? He had never taken an active part in politics but after all he had his own opinions and pet hates.

Well, it was in 1942. Your father was an active militant in a Resistance network. My husband denounced him to his brother Laurent, who hadn't yet joined the Militia at that time, but he was already well-established on the side of the collaborators. Laurent betrayed him to the Gestapo. He was deported to Mauthausen. No one knows how or when he met his death.

He had made me swear never to disclose the truth to you. He had his reasons but I'm sure that they no longer apply. He thought at that time that your happiness depended on not knowing our secret and that disclosing it would upset your whole life. He loved you deeply but felt that he had no right to your love, because he was not able to take on the duties and responsibilities of a father. He was married and had children. A miserable marriage. His wife was a dreadful drunkard. I judged her very harshly. It may be that she, too, was trying to forget something. I heard that she died three and a half years ago. Because of his children, because of that unhappy woman, he couldn't ask for his freedom and I never asked him to. If I wanted a divorce it was because I wanted to escape from the hell of my marriage. I should have set myself up in one little room with you. He wasn't rich but I would have been able to work. There were plenty of private schools which would have been glad of a graduate teacher.

You're not like him. For a long time I couldn't reconcile myself to that. Even that satisfaction was denied me. You're every inch a Toudroit. When I hear you speak, it's as if I was listening to Mama. But all the same, you're fond of music, and that isn't like either Toudroit or Servas. We used to go to a concert every week. He liked the Russians and Bartok. Amongst the classics, he was particularly fond of Bach. Now do you understand why I used to ask you to play the Brandenburg concertos so often? And finally, let me tell you that he was gay, generous and kind. He was the first cheerful man I had met since my father's death. My dear Dominique, you are serious like the Toudroits, but don't underrate the value of being gay and lighthearted. You need that sometimes to bear the weight of the world.

For eleven whole years I was happy, thanks to him and through him. We didn't ask too much. One hour together was enough to brighten the whole week. Perhaps it was because our time together was so short that our love didn't become tarnished and our hearts didn't harden as they do when they're too much in contact? It was just as if everything was always starting afresh. But I won't go on: that doesn't concern you and I doubt if you want to hear it; it's my own precious treasure which I'll take with me. It's good enough if you can just imagine it. Now I can understand why I told you all about Papa's little escapades. I wrote about them almost in spite of myself and while my pen was running on I even thought of all those experiments in automatic writing which were so fashionable when I was at university. So it was really just a weak attempt to justify your mother who had a bit of spirit in her, too. . . .

But those high spirits have had plenty of time to flag. I can't even start to tell you the slow horror of all my sufferings after the war. I had to live side by side with the murderer for sixteen years. I had realized what had happened as soon as Laurent was tried in his absence: the denunciation of your father to the Gestapo was mentioned in the charges. Laurent hadn't known him, so someone must have pointed him out to him. I had a dreadful scene with my husband and I accused him of doing it. He didn't even trouble to deny it. He was terrifying in his self-confidence, and quite imperturbable. I'm sure that not even the shadow of remorse crossed his mind. For him we were just vermin – the vermin that had settled on the dead bodies of the Auphals – the living dead as well. At first I thought of running away. But how – and where could I go? Work? I no longer felt strong enough. And then there was this: going away and leaving him would have meant making a break with the past and starting a new life. I didn't want to start anything new, and for me the past cancelled out any future. Staying with him meant not leaving the memory of your father. I doubt if you'll understand that. I never really understood it myself, and yet it showed me that our relationship with the dead is never a simple one and perhaps it made me better able to grasp my husband's relationship with his five brothers.

And then there was you. You were growing up and reaching the age when a child suffers at having to live alone with a mother who has left her husband. He had no affection for you but he was giving you an upbringing, as they say. It even seemed to me that his dislike of you was growing less. Later I realized that it was only apparent, and forced on him to keep up appearances: since he couldn't prevent other people from taking you for his son, he didn't want himself to be blamed for your failures. His pride was involved and his pride was boundless. So he followed your education with the dispassionate interest of the owner of a horse wearing his colours. Four years ago, he hardly cared whether your choice would have made you happy or unhappy: he merely didn't want it said that an Auphal, or Auphal in name if not in blood, had married a Jewess who was an anarchist. Once again, all this only became clear to me little by little. At the time, I believed that he was relenting. I thought that your future entailed the sacrifice of my present. Perhaps too I chose to follow what we usually call the straight and narrow way and which often enough is only a rut of stupid respectability. I didn't want you to be the son of a divorcee, just as Mama had been afraid that I might become an emancipated young woman. I'm not entirely a Servas either. After your ordeal of four years ago, I sometimes asked myself whether it was not the blood of the Toudroits that had told me me what to do. Your happy family life dispelled my fears. We hadn't made a mistake.

And so I've grown old between the memory of one man and love for my child. The memory hasn't faded but my love for you has grown until it has filled my whole life. In 1945, when I used to go every day to the Lutetia Hotel where they collected all those poor living skeletons who had barely escaped death and where they put up notices where I could never find his name, you were my lifebuoy. But for you I should have sunk without trace in my grief. Afterwards, you became my only reason for living, and in the end you became my whole life by your tenderness towards me. I was surrounded by a dreadful desert but we lived all those years together in the oasis of our love, didn't we? I was often afraid of smothering you with love and being too possessive. Now you are a man I can see that those fears were groundless. Dominique darling, I know that you make your wife happy, that your children adore you, that you are devoting your life now to the glorious task of maintaining France's influence overseas, but I must tell you that no one in the whole world owes you more gratitude than your mother whom you saved from despair and who, thanks to you, has died in peace. In this letter, which is really intended for *you*, I've been talking mainly about other people. But I don't need to tell my beloved son something that he knows already. Even if death comes to me unexpectedly, as it did to Nicholas, I shall die at peace with the world. Our hearts have been together for more than thirty years.

As for the other man, my husband, we put him on one side. I lived with him in gloom and apathy, enlivened only by flashes of hatred and anguish for what was past. Oh yes, I often asked myself whether it was not I who was responsible for the death of your father. As early as 1941 he had gone underground. He was fanatically active. He went to every corner of France. All our meetings were hazardous by now, in hotels where every time he had different identification papers. And then he would write to me. I didn't even bother to hide his letters. Is it through reading them that my husband got wind that he belonged to the Resistance? It's quite likely. I could never be certain. I was afraid of questioning him. And anyway there wouldn't have been any reply.

I must stop. My dear son, I don't really quite know what I have done. I've tried to free you from your childhood once and for all and from that father who wasn't your father, but haven't I written this letter really just as much for myself as for you? I still have time to destroy it. There's life in the old dog yet. And what will you be thinking of all this? Will it seem as if the heavens have collapsed on top of you, or will it just seem an ordinary commonplace bourgeois adultery such as one used to read about in novels? What will *your* verdict be? It was commonplace, I agree, but it wasn't ordinary. But it's true that when I was twenty I had dreams of another kind of life. Basically I took the wrong step when I went to study in Paris. But they soon dragged me back and made me toe the line. I was wrong to do it. And now, nothing has any importance any more.

I've released you from the man who wasn't your father, but I haven't succeeded in giving you back your real one. You see, the fact is that I still love him and always will. If he had survived,

207

perhaps our love would have died, like almost all love does. Fate willed it otherwise. We didn't part, we were parted. There's no gravestone to tell me for certain that he's dead, no date that would prove it to me every year. For a long time I fancied that he was living in some kind of Siberia or other, unable to come back to me. So if I let my pen run on, I shouldn't be talking about your father but all the time about the man I love. It's impossible. Of course, he was a hero too, a brave man, a tireless and energetic fighter. Of course, he was highly regarded in his profession. Of course, death probably stopped him from making a fine career. But I can only think of the smile in his eyes the last time I was with him. I can't possibly find words to express it and so I'll let him tell you himself. In the safe, the key to which is in my bag, you'll find photos of him and letters from him: all that remains of him for me. Some of his phrases will jar, some of his words will shock you. You must remember, my darling, that your mother wasn't always that dry old woman perpetually dressed in black, and understand that she was able to excite desire in a man and words to express that desire. Or better still, forget me and in those yellow old pages see only the picture of your father. I have trust that you won't be disappointed.

Dominique, my Dominique, when you read this letter I shall know the answer to the great question. As I write, it I must remain in doubt like all of us. But I still have the certainty that I shall see him again. Wait until you have lost a loved one and you will realize how that certainty can overrride any reasoning or any logic. I know it just as I know that you too will rejoin us both one day. Dominique, our Dominique, our beloved son, we shall be waiting for you ...

Mother

P.S. The routine details are all in my will which is with Maître Descaumont.

Appendix II

(Valérie Rossignat, the author of this document, was 51's mistress and fellow-student at the Institute of Political Studies. Their affair had come to an end long before she wrote this letter to 51, about one month before his marriage with 52. See also Appendix IIA.)

October 9th, 1958. Almost midnight!

This quick note by express to give you hell for having pitched us without warning into an unbelievable melodrama – it was like something out of Laclos. We still can't recover from the shock! Not everyone can be Merteuil, you know, and I'm afraid that distinguished Civil Servant Philippe, my husband, makes a pretty poor Valmont. Have you heard? If not, stop looking like Tarquinius and sit down pronto. If you have, here are some details. Your little fiancée from Normandy rang our bell about four o'clock this afternoon. I was out and about but my dear Philippe was cooking up some report or other in his study. When Maria showed her in, your young bride flung herself into his arms almost before the door was closed. It seems that she had sobs in her throat and tears lay like dew on her healthy cheeks. Philippe clasped her to his bosom, and finding one or two soft spots in her sturdy little body, tipped her on to the settee. Can you imagine. Sordid details: there are three springs broken. Maria must be killing herself. Thereupon, if I may coin a phrase, my dear Philippe gets his breath back and enquires the reason for his good fortune (I can see him now, the darling, cleaning his misted-up glasses after he'd adjusted his dress and trying hard to grasp what was happening, as always!). Your Liliane then flourishes an hysterical epistle from your anarcho-syndicalist bitchily congratulating her on bringing you back into the fold of the alienating bourgeoisie and going on to offer her, with her sincere good wishes for her future happiness, a few tips to remember for her wedding-night. I must admit that it was all pretty horrifying for a nice young lady brought up in the healthy breezes of the Cotentin, far from the foul miasmas of Paris. She hadn't left anything out: the long undisturbed sleep that one enjoyed in your bed (I protest! I protest!), your alleged idiosyncrasy of treating girls like boys (if that had been the case, I can't see why I needed to go off to Geneva ten days before the exams), your irony (the ungrateful girl!) and so on and so forth. All expressed with the utmost crudity and with details that, according to my adorable Philippe, left nothing to the imagination. Can you imagine? Thereupon (once again!) my distinguished Civil Servant Philippe puts on, I presume, his crafty look (the one acquired as a former pupil of our dear friends the Jesuits) and explains to your fiancée that it's not really all that serious, that barking dogs never stop the caravan from passing, that life is like that, that it won't be the last time, that what they have just done – which has no importance whatsoever, *whatsoever* – proves that a little sexual gymnastics doesn't add up to a tragedy, that moreover it's all over now, that the future belongs to her but she can't control the past and that she'll have to accept the fact that you had one or two little escapades before you met her ... Ouf! You can just imagine the sermon. So then your little Liliane snivels that she knows all about that and that she suspected that 'you knew about life' (isn't that wonderful?) but that wasn't the problem. The problem for her was in the moral turpitude disclosed by your anarcho-Trotskyist. She refused to marry Sade. Nothing less. Because after all, Dominouche, I don't want to offend you but ... And do you know what my Philippe replied? You'll never guess. This blockheaded technocrat slapped his thigh and exclaimed that of course he could completely reassure her on that point! Yes, my dear Dominette, he gave her the whole gen, she knows all, up to and including the fact that I also admitted that you were a satisfactory lover and no more abnormal than anyone else. Thereupon (still!) your young bride springs up like a Gorgon, tidies herself up (I have to imagine that because Philippe spared me the details) and dashes out screaming that it's a sink of iniquity, that we're all just a lot of perverted bastards, a Sodom and Gomorrha (is that how to spell it?), in short her exquisite lips gave vent to the foulest imprecations (!) that were of course religiously picked up by Maria and then, on her way downstairs, by Léonard, the upstairs tenant and, last but not least, by old Ma Minard, our charming concierge! Our honour is lost! But seriously, you can see what a scandal it's caused. I agree that my Philippe behaved like a clot, but after all he was trying to damp things down whereas your dear Liliane stands revealed as a complete and utter cunt. Girls like that ought to be called green-arse just as people are called greenhorns. But honestly, how can anyone even think of behaving like that! The more so as the little darling is not quite as brand-new as I thought (and how about you?). According to Philippe, the gate was already open, and pretty wide at that. So face the fact, even if it means losing some of your illusions, that some Norman squire or other, reeking of Calvados, had been there before you – or else, some farm-labourer fragrant with cow-dung. Or both, you can never tell with these little hypocrites. I suppose she's now going to fling her wedding dress to the winds and retire to the ancestral manor. All the better! Can you imagine the fuss every time you fancied a little romp with your Ambassador's wife? You'd never get any promotion at all. As for your anarcho-anarchist blue-stocking (a green-arse and blue-stocking, how colourful can you get, you lucky man!) her frightful letter merely bears out my countless warnings. That's what you get when you go to bed outside your own social circle. Really, what's happened is not even 'Liaisons Dangereuses', Laclos would have recoiled in horror: it's just being careless about who you associate with!

I must leave you to straighten things out with your two demoiselles by yourself. I've got enough to do sticking the pieces together where Philippe's concerned. He's pretending that the only thing that worries him is the public scandal. As for the rest, he just puts on his double chin and says 'Honours even'. Perhaps. Because after all we were doing our fornicating together in the august precincts of the Institute (not literally, of course! Can you

211

imagine old Siegfried's face if we had!) when Philippe was nothing more than a fellow-student sucking up to the prof, whilst he, the swine, has bedded your battered bride after two years of marriage during which I haven't strayed one inch from the straight and narrow, you hear. It doesn't matter, I'm rather fed-up but I don't question the umpire's decision. Honours even. I know my little Philippe with his butter-wouldn't-melt-in-my-mouth look. Our little episode had stuck in his gullet in spite of what he said. He wasn't at all unhappy at being able to tell me about his little session of petticoats up and trousers down. And he put on his three-chin-look when he asked me to tell you about it myself. It appears that you often told him that our affair mustn't at any cost disrupt your beautiful friendship. According to him (and you can imagine his jesuitical look when he said it) what has just happened will remove any danger of that. So you too are now both honours even.

I do hope, Domingo sweety-pie, that we're not going to fall out because of all this. It would be too stupid if we had to write to each other poste-restante to inform each other of the birth of our respective progeny. You know old Philippe, he's not the sort of man to crow. He's like you in that. I'm sure that you'll both spend many a dull evening happily rebuilding our glorious France. But not with the little Norman wench! If you marry her, my boy, all is over between us, you'll never darken my doorstep again! How can anyone be such a clot! I shall now pass a sleepless night working out how to repair the damage. Maria will either have to get the sack or a rise. Léonard is more straightforward, in the first place he's a bit hard of hearing, and I can always show him a bit more thigh going upstairs. The worst is old Ma Minard. She'll ruin my reputation in the quarter. Don't forget to give me a colossal cheque for her next Christmas box.

I press a thousand kisses on your burning brow . . .

Valérie

You men really are simple. My dear Philippe didn't understand a thing. Your Dulcinea may perhaps have come to be laid (vengeance!) but above all she wanted a bit of drama. If he'd held her hand for a couple of hours and kept talking, she would have gone away without any fuss at all. Instead, he acted like a medical board and passed you fit for active service, proof in hand, if that's the expression. What a cunt the man is!

Appendix IIA
(note pinned to
Appendix II)

You knew of course, didn't you, that I had intercepted this letter. You know too that it wasn't like me to do that sort of thing, and that I always scrupulously avoided interfering in your private affairs. But I could feel that you were going out of your mind and I felt that I was too, because of it. When I saw that letter arrive I had the intuition that it was going to cause further trouble. I wasn't mistaken. Oh Dominique, there you were surrounded by all those women like wild tigresses . . . I opened the letter and I read it and I took action. My first visit was to the woman whose love was clinging to you like the poisoned tunic of Nessus. I think that we found that we liked each other. She was already sorry that she had written her disgusting letter to Liliane. I got her to agree to say nothing and to disappear discreetly. Then I went to see Liliane. With her I took a hard line: she was to blame, not you. Your affair with Valérie Rossignat dated from the time you were at Sciences Pô together, whereas she, your fiancée, had deliberately flung herself into the arms of a man on the scandalous and defamatory evidence of a miserable woman who was out of her mind because she was losing you. I ordered Liliane to marry you straight away as the only way of preserving the honour of our two families intact. My third visit was going to be to Valérie. I wanted to ask her to say nothing to you about the whole thing – that unhappy girl's letter, Liliane's moment of weakness, her flippant and facetious letter – which I was then going to destroy. In this way you would have remained unscathed by all those sharp claws that were ready to tear at your flesh. But I didn't succeed in reaching Valérie in time and sparing you the horror of her disclosures. At least what I had managed to do first of all had exorcized the past and preserved the future. As your grandfather would have said, your mother hadn't let the grass grow under her feet!

And so after all this time here is Valérie's letter. I'm not returning it to remind you of what I may perhaps have been able to do for your happiness. I'm returning it to you first of all because it belongs to you, and secondly so that you may know that what it told me about you made no difference, no difference at all. When I finally managed to get hold of Valérie, she told me that you were sure that I had intercepted her letter and that, knowing how outspoken she is, you were worried at what I should think. Dominique, nothing that her child does can shock a mother. Yet you thought so. That's probably why you persist in feeling ashamed at talking to me about your relationship with Liliane. Even after ten years you seem to be reluctant to talk about it and you do so as little as you possibly can. I felt very hurt by that. I was even angry with myself for what I'd done because it had partly destroyed your trust in me. But I never really regretted it. It enabled you to be happy and so it didn't matter if it made me less happy. And now that words no longer have any importance, let me hand over this letter to you with the same confidence as I have handed over those that your father wrote to me.

Something else. You may perhaps think it a dreadful thing, but never mind. It's your happiness that I'm still thinking of. I know what men are like. Valérie said that you're simple. I think that above all you're weak. One day your body may give way to an impulse or your heart to a delusion. And like me, you're not very clever at pretending. Liliane will get to know of it. If that happens, show her Valérie's letter to refresh her memory. You two aren't honours even yet!

Poor Valérie, she didn't realize that her little game would be cut short so soon. I was quite fond of her, in spite of her manners.

Appendix III
(various objects –
descriptive list)

One coat of arms with the letters: Sc. Pô.

Two rusty metal penknives

One cigarette-lighter (u/s)

One broad leather belt (worn) with a buckle in the shape of a stylized Fleur-de-lys and inscribed 'Be prepared'

A bunch of 5 small keys (padlock type)

One piece of tinted glass (from sun-glasses)

One horn-handled penknife

One small piece of chamois leather

One horn-handled knife

Two epaulettes with one stripe (2nd lieutenant)

One French Army identity disc with 51's name and number 51.75-18780

One twisted fragment of light metal alloy labelled 'piece of English aircraft'

A case of fountain-pen cartridges

One magnet

One stone labelled 'Ammonite – Montreuil – Bellay – Maine et Loire'

One shell-splinter labelled 'Ack-Ack shell picked up in Chaville during the month of October 1943'

12 shell-splinters (unlabelled)

One rifle-cartridge case labelled 'During the attack on the Senate'

One badge of crossed hammer and sickle on a red background

One two-franc piece

One red military lanyard

216

One navy-blue forage cap
One photo of Marshal Pétain
One side-piece of pair of spectacles
One scout badge with T-shaped cross

Appendix IV
(Various documents –
descriptive list)

1) Card no. 4886 of Old Boys' Association of Collège Ladislas
2) French Scout card no. 433,518 stamped for the year 1947.
Province: Sainte-Geneviève. District: Vaugirard. Group: Cardinal
Dubois. Troop: Roland, 34th Paris.
3) Membership card of Friends of the Military Museum
4) French Army Personal Pay- and Service-Book
5) Physical Record Card issued by Paris University Club, 11
Rue Soufflot, Paris V, (basket-ball section) in 51's name

Date	Weight	Height
21. 2.48	136 lbs 6 ozs	5′ 5½″
11. 6.48	139 lbs 7 ozs	5′ 6″
14.10.48	138 lbs 11 ozs	5′ 6½″

Chest measurement expanded	Abdominal measurement at rest
38¼″	27½″
38″	28″
38⅛″	28⅜″
contracted	spirometer
34½″	4 1. 6
34″	4 1. 7
34¾″	4 1. 7

6) Voter's card issued by the Ministry of the Interior. Constituency: 6th Arrondissement, Section 3.

7) Copy of *Libération-Soir* newspaper dated Tuesday April 24th 1945. Headlines: 'THE RED FLAG FLIES ON THE CHANCERY OF THE REICH'

8) Copy of *Libération-Soir* newspaper dated Wednesday May 9th 1945. Headline: 'COMPLETE VICTORY'

9) Copy of *France-Soir* newspaper dated Wednesday May 9th 1945. Headline: 'IN A SCHOOL IN RHEIMS TWO PALE AND DISTRAUGHT GERMAN GENERALS PLEAD FOR CLEMENCY FROM THEIR VICTORS'

10) Part of a map showing Kiev-Warsaw-Odessa area. Pencil lines seems to be following the stages of the Russian advance in 1944.

Appendix V

Undated handwritten documents

(Photocopies available)

The Roland patrol leaders were surprised that you did not attend the Sunday parade, especially as it was a district parade and the honour of the troop was at stake. The court of honour will meet to decide what punishment to give you and give a decision on your case. If you have a proper reason for not coming, give J. Paul an excuse from your mother.

The Secretary (signature
illegible)

Punishment

832/HQC
Private 2nd Class Auphal, Dominique, 2 days CB
Charge: insolence towards a superior

Circumstances

Returning from guard-duty, Corporal Lanciné told me to have all the blankets displayed on the order of Sergeant Guisslin because the captain is going to inspect the room. The latter not only showed no respect for my seniority but even became abusive, showing jealousy of my rank. The incident took place in the presence of Corporal Lanciné and Private 2nd Class Sidibé Moussa.

Corporal Sylla Mamadou
Sentenced by 2nd Lt.i/c HQC: 2 days CB
(illegible)

On charge: Auphal

(text written by 51)

I can still see you now at the station, dear Patricia. You were so tiny, just a little girl in your cream-coloured raincoat. And the people around us were smiling as they looked at us. We queued up on the platform and then we found an empty carriage and so we went out again and walked up and down on the platform, and you kept looking at me with your earnest anxious little face just as you had the first time, peering from under your raincoat, in the field where I kissed you for the first time, and you said something that went straight to my heart, because you weren't used to saying anything tender: 'Oh, what a pity', and I was disappointed to learn later that 'pity' only meant *dommage* in French.

. . . Then we went back to the carriage where our compartment was and it was empty. And we stood in a corner of the corridor and kissed and kissed each other. You liked my French kisses and often it was you who put your arms round my neck and forced me to kiss you. And your little eyes were moist but alas, to my great despair, you weren't crying. Because I was waiting almost impatiently for you to go so that I could indulge in my thoughts of you and of your love for me.

And when the train was about to move off, I got down onto the platform with you, where I kissed my little Irish girl in front of all those Scots who were looking on and laughing. Then I had to get in again. And I lost sight of you. Finally I found the carriage door where we had been standing the moment before, and as the train gathered speed I kept kissing you at the window, little girl, and that was nice. And then you were farther and

223

farther away from me and you disappeared into the crowd around you and I couldn't see you any more. I went back very sadly to my compartment.

My first picture of you, Patricia darling, was the day when you were playing ping-pong with a Scottish boy. I saw and admired your graceful, slender figure and your lovely bust in a tight-fitting brown sweater. I can also remember you during the early days, when we were working at Fithie, standing in front of the shed where we ate and asking us, Robert and me, if we wanted to go and eat with the farm-labourers in their own room, and we refused, my darling, because during those first few days of the week we weren't very fond of the Scots in general and their girls in particular.

I can remember too the day I first began to pay court to you. We had been stooking in a field below the farm and, on the way back, I questioned you about your work and your age, and when I told you that I was 19 too you called me a child and I showed 'no sense of humour'. I wanted to be a man. That was why I had wanted to go and work with my hands in Scotland, harvesting, leave my family and be alone, whereas up till then I had always been in a group with the Scouts or the J.E.C. And I caught hold of you round the waist and spun you round. And I was already in love with you.

I can see you, too, asking me if I wanted to play darts with you and some other boys from Glasgow. And I agreed. But you played against me. And next week Vassa told me that he had looked at you while you were asking me, and he had seen that you loved me. And that made me very happy.

But my dearest memory, my love, is our first kiss. Do you remember? We were going to start stooking in that very big field, but we had to wait until the combine-harvester had cut a sufficient number of stooks. And one of the machines broke down. And we were sitting side by side. And Cathie wasn't there. And you had hidden your head under your raincoat and, playfully, I had tried to put my head under it too. We were each tugging at your mac and it got torn somewhere. You hid your face underneath it and I started to stroke the back of your neck, your ears, or rather, the left ear, and then I stroked your cheek and that very soft part of the face hidden away under the chin, and your skin was soft and cool and I loved you, my love. Then I stroked your nose,

224

which was incredibly small and up-turned. Then I half raised myself and I kissed your face (your nose was very cold) and I kissed your lips again, and this time you looked at me and I loved you. Then we had to go off to work . . .

I remember too, darling, the evening at the cinema at Kinnel. At first you were in front of me and I was just about to take the empty seat beside you, but Mike took it . . . I sat in front of you. Beside the Indian. And you were behind me, and each time I turned round I looked at you and very often our eyes met. In the end, exasperated by the stupidity of the film, I left before the end with Pierre and Sheila. I loved you, my sweetheart.

I remember too, the days following our kiss, but this time the memory is not pleasant. You let me sit next to you, but you weren't forthcoming. You let me kiss you, and when my hand started wandering you made this astonishing remark, little girl: 'Not here.' You were laughing at me, and you kept joking and laughing with the farm-labourers. You always went to and fro in the tractor and never wanted to get down and stay with me between trips. And I kept throwing stooks hard, straight at your face, and I didn't realize until the next week how much it hurt.

Remember the last evening, my darling, the Friday evening. In spite of all the snubs that I'd received (that very morning you had let me kiss you and then you had refused to come and eat with me in the shed 'because of Cathie', and you had been pulling my leg all the afternoon, with laughter in your eyes – wasn't it the day after our first kiss, even, and two days after the evening when I hadn't stopped watching you playing ping-pong, and you had lost every game you played because you were so put off!), I decided to make my last attempt! And I was playing ping-pong with the Indian and looking more at you than at the table. I was losing and you kept looking at me, pretending to be angry, puckering up your eyes and frowning in a charming fashion. When the game was over, I asked you, just like that, to come for a walk with me. And when the boy from Glasgow, the scout who gave me his belt, asked you what you would be doing after having a game, I think either with him or someone else, as you'd promised, you answered in a very determined voice, like some good little housewife, 'I'm going for a walk with Dominique', and that filled me with pleasure, my darling.

(poem written by 51)

For Jacqueline
18th October 1948

Autumn

Summer loves now turn to autumn leaves
But my heart greives
Along the Seine
Beside the tramps indifferent to my pain

Your hair is like a helm of ebony
Of Roman legionary
Greek hoplite warriors
Or cabin-boy beloved by sailors

The moist pink mist with the sun is wed
And clings to the gargoyles too
The barges of rusty hue
And hovers round Notre-Dame haloed in red

Your face aquiver with a sudden tremble
Your eyes of opal
Your mouth all indecision
Seem overcome now with a secret vision

The solitary islands all forgotten
The hideous old bridge beside
The now deserted river-side
    Your first kiss . . .
                        And a leaf has fallen

Appendix VI

Letters addressed to 51

(Photocopies available)

Balbigny, 14.6.1944

Dear Sir,

I am very happy to be able to write to you because I didn't have time before. You can keep the 10 francs. I'm sorry for you. Did you get home all right? I hope you'll write me a letter. Here's my address: Mr Michel Delille, c/o Madame Lenpetit, Rue de la Nation, Balbigny, Loire.

The weather has been wonderful but my sister is more stupid than ever. Today we are going for a bathe in the Loire. In our dump there is a cinema. We go there every Sunday. We saw 'Napoleon Bonaparte, and Perrette'. You saw that they have landed. It's not any too soon. Could you send me the Homework since Friday June 19th, because I've lost it. Did you manage to do your R.I. essay all right? I hope that you are not too bored and that you keep well.

I must go because I'm fed up of writing any more.

Goodbye and good journey!

Michel Delille

Paris, 20th June 1944

My dear Dominique,

It is a very long time since I heard from you, dear old chap, and you didn't even give me your holiday address. However, the Junior Member Section at Ladislas had a very successful end to the year. Although most of them cut the Farewell Mass, there were 23 of us out of about 30 present at the school for the farewell meeting on June 13th. Philippe Vitrier reported on your activities in Grade 5, and then his cousin Gérard, the team leader in Grade 4, did the same for his section and Pierre Falquet, team leader in Grade 3, completed the reports. Father Descozes said a word and Robert taught the juniors the J.E.C. anthem. We finished with the 'Chant des Adieux'.

16 Juniors are going to spend their holidays in Paris. Robert will be looking after them because I'm leaving Paris on Wednesday too. But the reason why I'm writing to you is because you haven't kept us informed as to what you're doing. And that would interest me, although perhaps you didn't realize it.

You see, my dear old chap, you agreed to become a Junior, to be a member of J.E.C. and even team-leader. The J.E.C. has undertaken to rechristianize France, with the J.O.C. and the J.A.C. I shouldn't like you to forget that you're a Junior, just because you've left school. I should be surprised if there are any Scout camps which you can go to now in view of all that's happening at the moment, but if you do find one, don't forget that you're still a Junior. Being a Junior means doing better than

230

anyone else in everything that you do and doing it for Christ. So you must be a super-Scout.

But I imagine that you'll be with your family in some quiet corner of France now. As I told you all during our meetings, a Junior's duties begin at home and now is the moment to show your 'guts' in your family. Don't be afraid of taking on any responsibilities that you feel able to do and helping your parents just that much. But you're on holiday now and your chief thought will be to play and enjoy yourself. You're right, old chap, and you must 'go to it' in your games. But remember that around you there will be farmers' sons of thirteen – your age – who will be looking after a hundred acres or more for their fathers who are prisoners of war, and that there are other children dying in Normandy.

That is roughly what I wanted to say to you, dear boy. Don't forget to keep in touch. Give my kind regards to your mother and remember me always as your dear friend in and for Christ Jesus.

Jean

231

Paris, 29th December 1946

Dear Dominique,

As every year at this time the Eagle Patrol send their best wishes for the New Year to their brother scouts, the Chamois. We hope that the Chamois Patrol will soon be sending the Troop some good scouts trained by them.

We hope too that our two patrols which came to have such great respect for each other during our competitions and contests in the camp in Cornwall will be having fresh encounters in the course of the coming year for the greater glory of our flags.

Fraternally yours,
Veau Académique

11/7/57

Now, now, my pretty one (you can see that I can remember your pet jokes very well), it was nice to read your flattering remarks, but in the world in which you live, where rape and murder are commonplace, is there really any room for flattery now?

I'm sorry you're no longer here – we're short on Attic salt at the moment. All these future officers and N.C.O.s are dreadfully earnest, not so much that they're thinking about what they're going to find in North Africa, but because they're worried about their final grading.

From a certain point of view, Saint-Maixent is just broad farce, an enormous Rabelaisian leg-pull with, however, the slaughter-house at the end . . . I'm trying to skive but it's not easy, especially since, in spite of all my efforts, I shall pass out as a section-commander and officer-cadet, whereas I should have been quite satisfied with sergeant.

I believe I told you that I'm in charge of the Saint-Maixent R.O. film club and I put on only pacifist or revolutionary films. This week it's 'La Bataille du Rail'. Some people – who must, of course, be raving mad – saw some connexion with the present situation. The army is subsidizing us to put on Potemkin. God, the army's *so* stupid . . .

Extra-curricular activities: the local middle-class set, composed of big-wigs and daughters of senior officers. I find myself frequenting it and flirting in hob-nailed boots with the daughter of

233

Major Pichard, president of the Reserve Officers' Club. You ought to be here: they're as funny as everyone else, where social relations are concerned. 'A game of bridge, you lovely girl: what lovely breasts you have . . . ' It's like an intermezzo on the stage with one's heart in one's boots. Did you move in this peculiar circle too? We've certainly been doing Sciences Pô an injustice. At least the girls were pretty.

I'm writing this letter from Paris, where I'm on leave for 10 days, doubtless my last. My parents are at Biarritz. I very nearly went to join them there. But the sight of the military disturbs me psychologically . . . And you know my father is one of that scum.

In a fortnight I get my stripe. Oh joy sublime, to have suffered in my turn a sea-change into . . . a warrior, a leader of men, a bloodthirsty condottiere like you, all set to disturb the peaceful nomads in the Aurès . . .

Did you know that Villars had managed to get himself killed?

I send you, my pretty one (and lieutenant to boot) my most deferential regards.

J.C.

You are to discover with the least possible delay the identity of the woman mentioned in Appendices I, II and IIA of your memo 2084 BZ of 2.5.1968 and described variously as: 'Jewish anarchist' (ref. 2085 SV), 'your anarcho-syndicalist' (ref. 2086 GB), 'your anarcho-trotskyist' (ditto), 'your anarcho-anarchist blue-stocking' (ditto), 'who clung to you like the tunic of Nessus' (ref. 2087 KC).

This woman might be identifiable with the woman whose photo is partially described under 10 in the list of contents of 51's wallet made by 5353 (v. Appendix 1999 HN to your memo 1991 NB of 10.11.1967) which, as we informed you in our memo 2063 DM of 27.3.1968, we consider an essential objective of operation DL 51.

Direct investigation with 51, 52 and their families must be rejected. The following individuals may be considered as offering possible sources of identification:

1) Isaure Champon
2) Simone Derelle
3) Hervé Bérasse
4) Philippe and Valérie Rossignat

The friendship between Isaure Champon and Simone Derelle on the one hand and 51 and 52 on the other would make any direct investigation of 51's and 52's private life risky inasmuch as Isaure Champon and/or Simone Derelle are liable to warn 51 and/or 52.

A similar risk exists where Hervé Bérasse is concerned, despite the slackening of his ties with 51/52 as a result of the loan which

235

has not been repaid.

It is on the other hand probable that the incident described in the material relating to Operation Lindbergh has put an end to the relationship between the Rossignats on one hand and 51 and 52 on the other.

Philippe and Valérie Rossignat will offer your first avenue of approach until such time as further intelligence, which must be assembled with all speed, may indicate if any approach is possible via Champon, Derelle and Bérasse.

Date: 8.5.1968
From: Mercury
To: Minerva
Subject: DL 51

Classification: TS
Ref. no. 2106 RA

1) 5672 reports that 5354 was caught by 53 on 1.5.1968 whilst engaged in sexual intercourse in the kitchen with the official chauffeur made available to 51 by the French Embassy in Delphi. 53 informed 52 who dismissed 5354. An appeal by 5353 on behalf of her daughter was unavailing. It is unlikely that 51 and 52 will take the matter to court. The supposition that 52 may take 5353 back into her service to replace 5354 can equally be discounted.

2) These facts lend additional urgency to the decisions to be taken regarding 55. We asked for instructions concerning her in our memo 2079 WB of 23.4.1968, to which no reply has been received. Since that time 8956 has reported to us that 55 has informed her family of her impending marriage. This news was received without enthusiasm by 55's parents, who urged her above all to go back to her former post with 52 in order to remove the bad impression caused by her abrupt departure. 5354's dismissal makes a further attempt on 52's part to get 55 back not unlikely. The latter, under pressure both from her parents and her former employers, might weaken if 8956 were to persist in further delay. Our assessment is that 55 offers very little further potential for exploitation, but that her return to Delphi might possibly result in her informing 51 and 52 of the enquiries made about them by 8956. We reiterate our request for your instructions and stress their extreme urgency.

3) Isaure Champon, described by 55 as a childhood friend of 52 (v. memo 2079 WB of 23.4.1968) has left Paris for six months. She is attached to the Centre National de la Recherche

Scientifique (CNRS) and will be undertaking in Oubangui-Chari research jointly financed by the CNRS and the Musée de l'Homme on circumcision rites amongst the Dambele tribes.

Date: 9.5.1968
From: Minerva
To: Mercury
Subject: DL 51

Classification: TS
Ref. no. 2107 BJ

1) A definitive decision regarding 55 can be taken only in relation to subsequent findings of Operation DL 51.

2) 8956 is to justify future delays by his reluctance to set 55 at loggerheads with her parents. He will call on them and endeavour to make himself agreeable to them. You will make a special grant of funds available to him. A long engagement would be most desirable.

3) 8956 will at once begin to accustom 55 to the idea that they might both go back and settle in Delphi after their marriage. He will refer to the uncertainty of his present occupation. The objective is to convince 55 of a possible resumption of her service with 51 and 52, with 8956 taking a job in Delphi, the nature of which can be settled later.

4) 8956 will arrange for 55 to write a letter to 51 and 52 announcing her marriage. 55 will ask to be forgiven for her abrupt departure.

5) Any immediate break between 8956 and 55 leading to 55's subsequent return to Delphi must be avoided at all costs. If the measures suggested in para. 2 prove inappropriate or inadequate it will be necessary to consider giving 55 a baby, since once she was pregnant she would become completely dependent on 8956 and would be forced to be patient.

Date: 9.5.1968
From: Minerva
To: Hecate
Subject: 8956

Classification: TS
Ref. no. 2108 DA

1) You will examine whether the cover of the above-mentioned agent is adequate to protect him from any screening process to which he might be subjected by the French security service.

2) If this is not the case, you will work out means of providing such adequate cover.

3) There is no urgency.

Dead Leaves IX

Attached herewith:

1. Typescript of the relevant portion of a conversation between 9000 and Philippe Rossignat, 38 yrs old, assistant secretary, Foreign Markets section, Ministry of Finance, residing 117 Rue du Conseiller-Colignon, Paris XVI. The recording was made on 8.5.1968 in the subject's office (tie-microphone).

2. Typescript of a telephone conversation between 8653 and Philippe Rossignat (9.5.1968).

His contact with the subject on 8.5.1968 having led to no progress in the identification of the objective, 9000 initiated a further attempt on the following day by means of 8653. He justifies his action by the following arguments:

1) His conversation with the subject on 8.5.1968 had lasted more than two hours, during which time a large number of names had been mentioned, thus excluding any possibility that the subject might have suspected any special interest in 51 on the part of 9000.

2) The subject revealed during the conversation that his contacts with 51 were infrequent and purely by correspondence.

The enquiries undertaken by 9000 and 8653 have given disappointing results. They prove that it will be very difficult to obtain accurate information concerning an episode in the private life of 51 and 52 from those familiar with them. This is all the more disappointing since of the five persons named in your memo 2105 DN of 3.5.1968 as being able to lead to the identification of the objective, Rossignat is the only one whom, thanks to the material produced by Operation Lindbergh, we know for certain to have had actual contact with the objective. On the other hand, the long-standing relationship between Rossignat and 9000 justified personal questions from the latter, which will not be the case for the agents who are approaching Hervé Bérasse and Simone Derelle.

1

Rossignat – and we've been blazoning it over the roof-tops for the last three years at the club/do you read our publications

9000 – I liked the state and the citizen/full of the right ideas but your fundamental error is wanting to fit theories which are a priori justifiable into sociological structures that aren't ready to receive them/in other words you want to graft new organs onto a social body with a far greater force of rejection than you appreciate

R – the students might prove to be our immunizing agents/did you see the damage at saint-germain

9000 – just a student procession that went off the rails/it wasn't the first time

R – I admire your equanimity

9000 – my dear man we managed to break the oas, so we can certainly do the same with the students/do you know how things are going at the école nationale/I suppose they still continue to take tea at five o'clock with typical british phlegm

R – the école is on the move/like everything else/even sciences pô is in a ferment/I dropped in only yesterday/jean saint-verjou he was your year wasn't he he was discoursing in the entrance hall in the middle of a group of students who seemed to be listening very closely I must say

9000	– a very brilliant young man saint-verjou/a wonderfully well-organized brain – very electric too/a really first-class man I even think that your previous minister was rather jealous of him/they were talking recently about his appointment to orva – or euratom I can't remember which
R	– surely not orva/auphal went there barely six months ago/saint-verjou at euratom/funny job for a financial expert/this government will certainly go down as having given the civil service a good shake-up its not even a shake-up its a rock and roll
9000	– the auphal you mentioned is the one from rabat
R	– he left the embassy a long time ago
9000	– it was the ben barka affair wasn't it/it was he who took up that very uncompromising attitude
R	– he's like you my dear fellow/a fanatical believer in the dignity and even the sanctity of the state/he's just your sort of man/I know him well/we were at sciences pô and the école nationale together/ dominique's a friend of mine
9000	– I must have met him somewhere two or three years ago/I've got a vague memory of what he looks like but I remember his wife very much better/a very pretty young woman
R	– liliane's a charming girl
9000	– oh dear the way you said that/you sounded very judicial/I hope I haven't spoken out of turn
R	– no not at all old man/it's just that I was a friend a real friend of dominique's but our wives didn't get on/these things happen
9000	– forgive me
R	– oh it's all over now/now that valérie is no longer here all these little contretemps have fallen into perspective/I don't see dominique now any more but we write to each other occasionally/in fact I received a letter from him this week which throws interesting light on the ben barka affair/you know he's developed a lot since rabat/are you interested
9000	– don't tell me that he's found the dead body in the

cellars of orva/yes I know I shouldn't say that/yes
read it to me it interests me a lot

R   – chinese infiltration in central africa/um I'll skip/a
diatribe against the fourth republic/he really can't
restrain himself/I get that every letter/ah here we
are/yesterday I met gilbert varlot who's in charge of
our commercial section in frankfurt

9000   – varlot/I know him quite well/same year as me

R   – in frankfurt/former civilian comptroller in morocco
during the empire/I expected the perennial what we
ought to have done in inverted commas and the
usual description of the glaouis cavalry outside the
gates of rabat but old varlot is not the nostalgic type/
we talked about oufkir whom varlot knew very well
before the end of the protectorate and whom I knew
after it/we agree about him/with perhaps rather
greater reservations on varlot's part I made him
smile when I described to him the episode of oufkir
getting out of his helicopter like an exterminating
angel to cut the throat of a dissident tribesman with
his own hands/but he uses the diabolical character
of oufkir as an argument in favour of his innocence/
let me sum up what he said/oufkir is capable of
anything including cutting an enemy up into shreds/
but he will always do it efficiently/if he decided to
eliminate a whole village completely you wouldn't
find a trace either of the villagers or the methods
used to do it/so the fact that he was in paris when
ben barka was kidnapped is enough to prove his
innocence he would never have been so stupid as to
be present on the scene of a crime that was being
committed by him/I replied that only the evidence
of a student who was with ben barka had prevented
him from being whipped away without anyone being
any the wiser but varlot objected/no doubt rightly/
that b.b. had arranged to meet someone in paris/that
his disappearance would in any case have become
public knowledge and that they wouldn't have failed
to link it with oufkir's presence in paris/so much for

245

the defence/I tried unsuccessfully to put forward the arguments on the other side/varlot backed his personal belief/completely subjective of course and quite impervious to logic/that if oufkir had been guilty he would have set about it differently/I couldn't persuade him otherwise

9000 — yes old varlot was known for his pigheadedness/but a very sound man please note/I'd be tempted to think he's right

R — I can't say I don't know him/let me go on/had I met him at the time of the affair I shouldn't even have listened to what he was saying/but time has made me think/if it's true that the whole question is to know who benefited from the crime then it's possible to see things more clearly now/b.b. being assassinated just when he was getting ready to launch a crusade on behalf of the third world/and even a fierce opponent like you knows that it wasn't a crusade against us/our government tottering to the great satisfaction of certain people abroad who find our foreign policy intolerable/our relations with morocco reaching breaking-point a power vacuum being created there which since then we've seen others rushing to fill or anxious to fill/do you follow me/and in addition the fact that french security forces were involved seems very significant for anyone like myself who knows that those services even after ten years of gaullisme are still full of cia cells and manipulated by them/does this mean that I'm going to canossa after wanting to burn rabat/ certainly not/but I'm less sure of my own view/old varlot has made me very very perplexed/I'd heard his theories before and I'd listened to them with a certain interest but I must confess that I was shaken to hear them defended with such conviction and pleaded so skilfully/I was one of those who didn't forget and every day when I opened my paper I hoped that I might see the truth printed there loud and clear/I'm not sure that I want that any more/how

stupid we'd look if tomorrow or in a year's time or
in five year's time it turns out that all of us french
and moroccans as well were just the puppets in a
farce in which washington was pulling the strings/
well what do you say to that

9000 — it's interesting/hypothetical of course but interest-
ing/do you believe in this so-called infiltration of the
french secret service

R — my dear man in that sphere I'm tempted to believe
everything and determined not to believe anything/
ah will you excuse me/hallo/yes speaking/good
afternoon sir/yes of course/I'll come at once/I'm
terribly sorry the boss wants to see me

9000 — of course old boy you must go where duty calls/good
heavens/it's four ten/can I use your phone

(ends)

2

8653	– hallo might I have a word with monsieur rossignat please
R	– speaking
8653	– is that monsieur rossignat
R	– yes
8653	– monsieur rossignat in person
R	– yes it's monsieur rossignat speaking in person
8653	– I'm sure you don't remember me
R	– is it you catherine/hallo is that you catherine/look please stop this it's ridiculous
8653	– no I'm not catherine/you must forgive me perhaps I'm disturbing you
R	– you're not disturbing me you're just worrying me/ who on earth are you
8653	– you don't know me/we've never met
R	– what can I do for you then
8653	– I'd like you to give me back my letter/I'm getting married you understand so you see I'd be unhappy to know that it's still in existence and that it may turn up you never know/I'm rather ashamed of myself/I regretted writing it as soon as I'd sent it
R	– I see/now let me try to understand/we've never met but all the same you wrote me a compromising letter that you want back/is that it
8653	– yes except that it's not a letter I wrote to you/but to dominique's fiancée

248

R	– dominique auphal/oh I see/I'm beginning to understand what you're getting at/so you must be sarah
8653	– you see you don't even remember my name
R	– my dear girl I never knew it in the first place/if I recall aright your little love missive was signed sarah that's all/but the point is that I haven't got your letter/I never did have it/what makes you think that it might be in my possession
8653	– at the time dominique told me that his fiancée had brought it to show you
R	– she did bring it she did show it me and she took it away again/I suggested to her that she should destroy it/yes that's what happened I even offered to burn it in my fireplace but she wouldn't hear of it/I think she was determined to show it to her father
8653	– oh I see/that's very disappointing for me I hoped that you would give it back to me
R	– the simplest thing would have been not to write it/in any case I can't return it to you because I haven't got it/but I can't really follow your problem/you're going to get married/splendid let me congratulate you/and so what if you hadn't rung me this happy event would have escaped notice and even if by some extraordinary coincidence I had heard about it you don't think surely that I would send your love letter to your dear fiancé for information/you mustn't judge others by yourself you know
8653	– you've got a low opinion of me haven't you
R	– you've got a low opinion of yourself if I understand what you were saying correctly/look you know as well as I do that you nearly made them break off their marriage but only nearly that's the point/they did get married and I think they are happy and I'm sure they've got lots of children/well two anyway that's something/OK you're going to get married you're going to have children wonderful so do you think it's absolutely necessary to stir up the past/get married and to hell with the letter that you were

249

	bloody stupid enough if you'll pardon the expression stupid enough to write ten years ago
8653	– it's really just that I'm ashamed/it's a stain on my character/on my past/I'd like to have a clear conscience before starting my new life
R	– I see/well sarah your feelings of contrition do you credit and I'm delighted to hear about them but I'm sorry to see that you're just as dreadfully complicated as you were ten years ago
8653	– wouldn't it worry you to begin a new life when you've got such a frightful thing as that letter in your past
R	– the thing which would worry me above all would be having written it/tell me/there's one solution/if you're so keen we could resuscitate your letter/I've forgotten the exact words but if we both tried very hard I'm sure that we can succeed in reproducing what they described/I haven't forgotten that/what do you think
8653	– I think that you're revolting
R	– my dear girl you remember what valéry said/there are boring women damned boring women and bloody boring women/and I think you qualify without any trouble at all for the last category
8653	– what a beastly man you are

(ends)

Date: 13.5.1968
From: Minerva
To: Pythoness
Subject: Identification 51

Classification: TS
Ref. no. 2112 HA

Herewith data card of a person likely to be stored by you by reason of her extreme political opinions.

Urgent. Please keep informed as results come in.

One enclosure

NAME	: –
FIRST NAME	: Sarah
SEX	: F
DATE OF BIRTH	: Unknown. Present age between 25 and 45
PLACE OF BIRTH	: –
FAMILY CONNECTIONS	: –
RACE	: Jewish
NATIONALITY	: Presumed to be French
HEIGHT	: –
WEIGHT	: –
EYES	: –
HAIR	: Presumed to be black
SPECIAL PECULIARITIES	: –
RELIGION	: –
EDUCATION	: University level, no subjects specified
PROFESSION	: –
PREVIOUS ADDRESSES	: Living in Paris in 1958

PRESENT ADDRESS : –
MARITAL STATE : –
SEXUALITY : Heterosexual in 1958, not known if bisexual
POLITICAL OPINIONS : In 1958 militant Trotskyist or Trotsky sympathizer or militant anarchist or anarchist sympathizer
SPECIAL REMARKS : –

Date: 13.5.1968
From: Minerva
To: Mercury
Subject: DL 51

Classification: TS
Ref. no. 2113 LC

1) The relationship between Rossignat and 9000 justified using the latter to approach the subject. On the other hand we disapprove of 9000's action in arranging, on his own initiative, for the subject to be rung up by 8653 on the day after his visit. The fact that 9000 felt it necessary to justify his action proves that he was himself perfectly aware that it was a rash thing to do. You will instruct 8653 to confine herself in future to her role as contact and to abstain from any action that she has not been ordered to undertake by her superiors. You will inform Socrates that we are requesting Jupiter to issue a reprimand to be recorded in her personal file. You are to remind 9000 that he is too important a source to be allowed to initiate operations the results of which are totally disproportionate to the risks involved. We are aware that his unfortunate taste for conspiratorial activity makes 9000 difficult to handle, but this shortcoming should be counterbalanced by an even greater vigilance on your part and on that of Socrates.

2) A data-processing selection has been made on the basis of the material collected on Sarah X. Pythoness has named 18 persons corresponding to the data submitted. You will start your investigations with a view to discovering the identity of the subject immediately on receipt of the relevant files or records from Clio.

Date: 17.5.1968   Classification: TS
From: Hecate   Ref. no. 2114 KR
To: Minerva
Subject: 5353

In your memo 2065 LS of 27.3.1968 you ordered screening procedure 1 to be applied to the above-mentioned agent, extending to her immediate family circle.

The appropriate machinery was set in motion on 1.4.1968.

As yet no suspect contacts with any rival security services by the three persons concerned have been detected. Their standard of living is in accordance with their official salaries plus their additional income from us. They show no evidence of possessing particular political views.

Observation is continuing.

Date: 25.5.1968
From: Mercury
To: Minerva
Subject: DL 51

Classification: TS
Ref. no. 2115 TS

Dead Leaves X

8047 has collected information about Bérasse, Hervé, journalist, residing at 116 Boulevard Flandrin, Paris XVI. 8047 was operating under the cover of inspector on behalf of a hire-purchase firm.

The subject, aged 37 or 38, is known in the district as leading a disorderly life with numerous affairs with women, and as having recourse to financial expedients to maintain his way of life. It is said that he is being sued by a number of people for non-payment of bills. He has changed cars three times in the last six months. None of them has yet been paid for. Most of the tradesmen in the district have stopped giving him credit. His charwoman has not been paid for three weeks. The subject is said to be unaffected by his precarious financial situation. He is alleged to be promising his creditors speedy repayment thanks to a monthly periodical which will shortly appear under his editorship.

Enquiries made by 8047 in journalistic circles confirm that Bérasse is preparing to bring out a monthly devoted to holiday and leisure activities. He is well known in these circles since he has been working for the last fifteen years for a large number of Parisian periodicals or dailies. He has not got a good reputation. He is mentioned as having invented interviews or incidents which he reported. His wide circle of acquaintances, his glibness and his lack of inhibitions enable him to find sporadic employment as a crime-reporter. Three years ago he was supposed to be launching a monthly entitled: 'Our Brother Animals' but is said to have dropped the project after having extracted large sums of money for advance publicity from firms manufacturing pet-food and animal foodstuffs.

Having obtained this information, 8047 contacted the subject on the afternoon of 13.5.1968, posing as the deputy advertising manager for a Hispano-Belgian property company constructing holiday residences on the Santander coast.

Recording proved impracticable since 8047 was received by the subject in a room where three people were talking loudly and a radio was on all the time (the present events in France also caused delay in transmitting this report).

8047 stated that he was looking for publicity for his property company. He said that Bérasse's name had been given him by a friend of 52. Bérasse spoke briefly of his connexion with 52. He stated that he had got to know her through her sister Geneviève de Maupertain, the wife of Dermoy, through having interviewed her in 1953 when he was working for a monthly magazine devoted to tennis. He said that 52 had met 51 at a party given by himself.

The conversation was interrupted by the radio news. It was not possible to pick up the threads of the conversation about 52 because Bérasse and his friends were making angry comments on a demonstration that was taking place in Paris at the time.

The subject asked 8047 if his firm would be prepared to make an advance on account for future advertising space. He was plainly disappointed when 8047 refused to commit himself. He then put an end to the conversation. 8047 promised that he would make contact with him again as soon as the periodical appeared in order to fix up the advertising contracts as appropriate. The subject showed no interest in this promise and gave 8047 the impression that he himself does not believe that the review will be published.

8047 concludes that it will be pointless to make further contact with the subject unless at the same time making financial propositions to match. We leave you to consider this possibility in principle and estimate the amount involved.

Date: 6.6.1968
From: Mercury
To: Minerva
Subject: DL 51

Classification: TS
Ref. no. 2117 BP

In your memo 2113 LC of 13.5.1968 you informed us that Pythoness had selected 18 persons possibly identifiable with Sarah X.

Clio forwarded to us on the same day 3 files and 15 record cards.

Despite the difficulties in our link with France, we managed to transmit our instructions to Socrates.

Socrates immediately deployed all available personnel on the necessary investigations.

Sarah Roboul was located on 18.5.1968 i.e. five days after the launching of the operation (13.5.1968).

8848 contacted her on 24.5.1968 and had full and satisfactory sexual intercourse with her on 25.5.1968, during which he obtained confirmation that:

1) Sarah Roboul had been 51's mistress in 1958.

2) She was the woman described in various terms in Appendices I, II and IIA of our memo 2084 BZ of 2.5.1968.

3) She was the woman whose photo is listed as item 10 in the list of contents of 51's wallet made by 5353 (Appendix 1999 HN of our memo 1991 NB of 10.11.1967).

The question of exploiting this person gives rise to the following reservations:

1) As in the case of Hervé Bérasse, the present situation in France has resulted in reducing the possible scope of the investigation. The grave events that are taking place in Paris are having the effect of polarizing the persons concerned on the

present to the detriment of the past. This is the reason why 8848's report does not fulfil all that might have been expected from contact with the subject.

2) The relationship that has been established between 8848 and the subject might be considered as nullifying this temporary obstacle inasmuch as it seems likely to outlast the present disturbances, thus enabling us to expect a more substantial supply of intelligence from the subject in the future. We feel bound to point out that reading 8848's report has aroused a certain apprehension in us by reason of the tacit sympathy that it disclosed towards the subject. We recall that 8848's political tendencies have twice led to a Hecate screening, the outcome of which was considered satisfactory by Jupiter. 8848 has been successfully employed on several occasions in the exploitation of subjects of Roboul's sort, whom he seemed more suited to handle and exploit than anyone else by reason of his personal leanings. The fact remains that 8848 represents a certain security risk and that a certain element of passion, traces of which can be discerned in his report, might considerably increase his factor of unreliability.

We are forwarding information collected by Socrates on ten of the eighteen subjects investigated direct on Clio to enable them to up-date the relevant files and record-cards. Socrates called off the investigation of the other seven as soon as Sarah Roboul had been identified.

Enclosures: Report DL XI by 8848 and one attached document

Dead Leaves XI

1. Approach

Operational data supplied by Socrates on 17.5.1968 at 2200 hrs.

On 18.5.1968 enquiry at the address indicated, 43 Rue Guy de la Brosse, Paris V. The subject moved four years ago. Enquiry at a series of her addresses: 75 Square Desnouettes, XV, 33 Rue Palatine, VI and 180 Rue Campagne Première, XIV, where the subject is residing at the moment. The concierge stated that the subject had not been seen for several days and provided a description. Observation with no result.

19.5.1968, observation with no result
20.5.1968 ditto
21.5.1968 ditto
22.5.1968 ditto
23.5.1968 ditto

On 24.5.1968 at 1325 hrs the subject returned to the block at 180 Rue Campagne Première and left again at 1412 hrs after a change of clothes.

Subject shadowed to the Sorbonne.

2. Contact

Contact was made at the Sorbonne on 24.5.1968 at about 2000 hrs under assumed identity, on the excuse of helping the subject provide first-aid treatment for students injured in the current demonstration.

On 25.5.1968 at about 1200 hrs the subject was accompanied

home from the Sorbonne. Complete and satisfactory sexual intercourse with the subject at her home. Returned to the Sorbonne at about 1800 hrs. On 26.5.1968 at about 0200 hrs the subject became unwell as the result of overwork and excessive use of stimulants. Talked until 0800 hrs, returned to her home and then separated in order for this report to be drawn up.

3. Description

The subject's passport contains the following details: height: 5' 5¾"; colour of eyes: black; special peculiarities: none. The subject weighs approx. 121 lbs. Short black hair. Domed forehead. Eyebrows partly plucked. Black eyes. Small ears with attached lobes. Short nose. Fleshy lips. Three gold-crowned molars in top left, one gold-crowned molar in lower left. Small breasts. Extremely narrow waisted. Bulbous hips. Prominent pubis. Two birthmarks, one on the left arm over the biceps, the other on the stomach, one hand's breadth to the left of the navel. A strawberry mark approximately the size of a fingernail on the right buttock. Appendicitis scar. Extreme short sight involving the use of contact lenses.

4. Biography

The subject was born on 15.7.1934 in Constantine (Alger ia), daughter of David and Golda Liberstein, spring vegetable growers.

She suffered grave trauma as a result of the anti-semitic measures taken by the Vichy Government during the Second World War. She says that she was banned from attending school. This personal experience and the revelation of the extermination camps in 1945 made her conscious of being specifically Jewish. While still very young she decided to emigrate to Israel. This plan was agreed to by her parents. She left for Israel in 1952 and lived for nine months in a Kibbutz close to the Syrian border. The experiment ended in failure, as she did not succeed in becoming integrated into Israeli society, which she describes as 'a bunch of bigots who haven't yet found a Voltaire'.

She settled in Paris in 1954 and commenced university studies in the humanities. She lived on a small allowance from her parents plus additional earnings from activities such as baby-sitting etc. Her militant activity in left-wing organizations dates from this period. It is probable that her political orientation was motivated in the first instance by her belief that anti-semitism would only be ended by the introduction of a socialist social system. Later the subject became progressively less specifically Jewish-centred in her political opinions and based her left-wing attitude more on anti-colonialism than on the struggle against anti-semitism. She joined the French communist party in 1955 but left it again in 1956 in view of the reluctance of the party to take a firm stand in favour of Algerian independence. A few months later the subject joined a network supporting the Algerian 'Front de Libération National' (F.L.N.). She was interrogated by French security services (D.S.T.) on an indeterminate date. Released through lack of proof, she nevertheless remained under observation and was forced to break off contact with her network. She then moved in anarchist or Trotskyist circles in Paris, but was disillusioned by their empty verbiage. She also accused them of being victims of police infiltration. In this respect it is interesting to note that the subject's participation in the struggle of the Algerians in Paris has given her a first-hand experience of underground activities.

The end of the Algerian war inaugurated a period of doubt and withdrawal from politics, which came to an end only with the Chinese cultural revolution and above all with the recent events in Bolivia. The execution of Che Guevara and the trial of the Frenchman Régis Debray have led to a remarkable revival of interest in politics by offering her a new field of political action. She tried to go as a teacher to Cuba but was rejected by the Cuban authorities on the grounds of her ignorance of the Spanish language. Although disappointed by this failure she fairly quickly recovered and helped organize little groups of Guevara supporters in Paris.

The subject's present political views are very difficult to pin down because she has retained a little of each of the numerous movements or parties to which she has belonged or which she has supported. In order to be exhaustive, one would have to refer to

261

her as a supporter of communism, anarchism, Trotskyism, Maoism and Guevara, not forgetting that she is also a Zionist since, although she brands Israeli politics as 'imperialistic and reactionary', she admits that whatever the circumstances, she wants the Jews to win.

The subject's basic motivations are probably easier to define than the political commitments to which they gave rise. Her instinctive reactions make her automatically side with victims of any sort (Jews during the Second World War, Algerians during the Algerian war, Castro-type guerrillas in Bolivia, etc.) and her various political commitments may be interpreted as representing a series of attempts to give a coherent structure to her sentimental impulses. Her attitude towards Israel is in this respect particularly significant. In fact, whilst her reason leads her formally to condemn Israeli politics, she yet supports the Israelis unconditionally, not so much because of racial solidarity as by reason of their inferiority in numbers and the fact that they are encircled: these circumstances turn these (objective) imperialists into (subjective) victims. It is obvious that the subject's behaviour is strongly tinged with romanticism and we should hardly be exaggerating were we to conclude that whilst belonging to or supporting various, sometimes contradictory, political movements, she has never ceased being, at least in spirit, a member of the Salvation Army. She has plunged headlong into the present riots which offer a perfect outlet for her romantic activist leanings. In this respect, it is interesting to see that the subject has refused the leading role to which she could justifiably have laid claim in view of her status as university teacher and is content with the relatively modest task of first-aid worker. In this role she shows considerable energy, tireless devotion and a complete disregard for danger.

As far as her family circle is concerned, the subject confined herself to saying that she had quarrelled with her parents at the time of the Algerian war. Her father and mother were former supporters of the 'Organization Armée Secrète' (O.A.S.) and live at Nice (Alpes-Maritimes) where they keep a newspaper kiosk.

The subject was uncommunicative as to her professional activities. She is assistant lecturer at the Faculté des Lettres of Paris University.

5. Exploitation

Whilst the pre-revolutionary situation in Paris facilitated making contact with the subject, it has complicated her exploitation by reducing the possibility of conversation and polarizing the subject on the present at the expense of the past.

No exploitation was possible from about 2000 hrs on 24.5.1968 to about 1200 hrs on 25.5.1968.

Of the five hours spent at the subject's home, four were spent sleeping after full, satisfactory but brief sexual intercourse. It was possible to verify, in accordance with Socrates' instructions, that the subject was not averse to anal insertion.

The indisposition which affected the subject at about 0200 hrs on 26.5.1968 enabled a limited exploitation since it prevented her from continuing her first-aid work in the emergency casualty post set up in the Sorbonne. She was unable to go to sleep, probably owing to the excessive quantity of stimulants which she had taken. She was in a state of extreme nervous irritability, talked disjointedly and at times almost deliriously and seemed to be reenacting in nightmare fashion the scenes of violence which she had witnessed the previous night. A volunteer doctor administered a tranquillizer at about 0300 hrs. This caused temporary prostration in the subject, on recovering from which she launched into a political monologue from which the information reported above was pieced together. It was very difficult to lead the conversation on to her love-life and on to 51. Once this was achieved it proved impossible to extract detailed information from her in reply to any queries since, although much calmer than before, she remained in a kind of trance, talking in a monotonous tone without seeming to hear the questions she was asked.

The subject met 51 in January 1958 in unspecified circumstances. 51 had just returned from Algeria. The subject, who had recently been forced to give up her underground activities in support of the F.L.H., said that she had in the first instance been interested by what 51 had to say about his Algerian experiences. According to the subject, 51 was at that time considerably confused in mind as a result of his military experiences which, still according to the subject, had been the first time he had had to face up to the real world. For her part, the subject was going through a difficult period as a result both of having been forced

263

to give up her underground work and of her disillusionment at the futility of the Trotskyist and anarchist organizations. According to the subject, it was these mutual difficulties which brought them together in feelings of sympathy which quickly turned into love and full and satisfactory sexual intercourse. The subject is sure that she was 51's first and only love. She admits that she herself had previously engaged in a number of affairs but these were with Party comrades whose political beliefs excluded any sort of normal private life and any sentimental love-life, which was considered by them a waste of time. According to the subject, 51 was a typical example of bourgeois alienation. He had been brought up in a very conformist family and had greatly suffered by a conflict with his father. She considers that 51 was afflicted with a particularly powerful Oedipus complex. His childhood and adolescence followed a typically bourgeois pattern: educated in a Roman Catholic private school, member of the Scouts and of the J.E.C. (Jeunesse Etudiante Chrétienne). 51's only attempt to break through what the subject called his class-barriers was a trip to Scotland at the age of about eighteen to help with the harvest. At the time the subject met him, 51 was not looking forward to the administrative career on which he was about to embark. She claims that he was much influenced by her political theories, which provided him with the answers to some of the questions that he had been led to ask himself during his period of service in Algeria. Convinced that 51's personality was being stifled by his family environment and social conditioning the subject endeavoured to persuade him to break with them. Despite her urging, 51 refused to agree to be psycho-analysed, which the subject considered would have helped him to get rid of his Oedipus complex. He agreed to write a short story (v. enclosure) which in spite of its formal weaknesses, proves, according to the subject, that 51 had literary gifts and that writing might even act as a substitution-therapy for his personal problems. All her efforts came to naught since in the end, to use the subject's own expression, 51 was retrieved by his class. 51's family had exerted great pressure on him by appealing to his family feeling as well as by stressing that in living with an extremist he would be barring the way to any senior administrative position and lose caste, so that his brilliant academic career would have been wasted. But, according to the subject, the fundamental reason why she was unable to prevent 51's return to his family was the Oedipus complex caused by 51's guilt-feelings towards his father which kept him in a state of passive obedience despite his age. The parting took place in unpleasant circumstances because, according to the subject, 51 hid his capitulation to social and family pressures under the ostensible excuse of his sudden love for an uninteresting young middle-class girl whom he in fact did not really love but was using merely as a pretext to break with the subject.

It is plain that the subject has continued to harbour feelings towards 51 that may be described, at least, as tender. During a chance encounter two years ago, 51 is alleged to have told the subject that he had only ever loved her and that he now regretted not having taken her advice. It was on this occasion that he produced an old photo of the subject which he kept in his wallet and which he had torn up and covered in pin-pricks at the time of their parting. It was not possible to discover whether the subject and 51 had sexual intercourse on that occasion, since, as stated above, the subject did not reply to the question.

6. Future possibilities

Since the contact was made in romantic circumstances, particularly attractive to the subject, it is probable that this affair may be continued for a certain length of time in conditions which will enable a better exploitation of the subject.

Enclosure: typewritten manuscript of 51's short story, which was handed over, without any demur by the subject, on the morning of 26.5.1968.

The Splinter

At six o'clock in the evening, the officers announced, vociferously, that the exercise had been a balls-up and that they would begin again after nightfall. The officer-cadets reassembled on the dried-up bed of the wadi, and lined up as best they could, stumbling over the boulders as they did so. Their faces were ruddy and there were dark circles of sweat on the armpits of their dungarees. They were talking loudly and seemed annoyed. The paratroopers sat watching them in a little group apart. He was one of the six paratroopers; squatting beside Sergeant Marat, he was wondering what was the point of the whole thing. You can't teach troops how to detect a Fell ambush laid in a wadi. To his mind, the problem was not so much avoiding the ambush – you never could avoid it anyway – as to know how to get out of it when half your men had been knocked out by the first burst of fire from the Fells. You can't learn that sort of thing in any exercise, and he wondered even whether the cadets were interested in learning it. Having been landed in Algeria after three months' preliminary instruction, for the next six months they were going to attend the officer-cadet field-training course that had just been set up at Zellifa. Their conceited, rather sullen faces hardly matched the youthfulness of their features, which were already tired and drawn. He noticed that their weapons were covered in dust and that several of them, in the excitement of the exercise, had put the safety catches of their MAT 49s in the firing position. Some of the MATs from Indo-China were so badly worn that a burst of fire could be triggered off by the slightest jar. He thought to himself

266

that he wouldn't like to take part in an operation with blokes like that and he stood up together with Sergeant Marat because one of the platoon lieutenants was coming over towards them. The sergeant saluted by bringing his hand to the peak of his cap, not to above the ear as laid down in regulations: for some weeks now it had been the fashion in the regiment to salute like the Germans.

*

The kitchen had been set up a short distance away from the training camp, amongst some cork-oaks. They were lent five mess-tins and knives and forks. Sergeant Marat had been invited to eat with the platoon N.C.O.s. They watched the cooks lift the enormous pot of soup off the stove. The head cook was tall and thin. He was wearing a bowler hat and spoke with a Paris accent. When his assistants had placed the pot in front of him, he let the paratroopers help themselves, then opened his flies, pulled out his old man and gave a quick spurt into the soup saying: 'Here's to our future leaders'. Then they had sausages, mashed potatoes and an apple. They drank, a quarter of a litre of wine, but refused the offer of the head cook when he suggested having a piss-up. After that they had to leave the kitchen and went and sat down in a small open space enclosed by four barrack huts.

Leaning against the wall, with their tanned faces glowing in the last rays of the sun, they watched the officer-cadets coming out of the dining-room in small groups, and they could see that the rest and the food had done them good. They were laughing as they talked, and they looked fresh and replete, with their belts loosened. The dining-room must have been steamed up because those wearing spectacles were wiping them with clean handkerchiefs. With their noses stuck up in the air, they were talking nineteen to the dozen. Some of them were even walking slowly along with their hands behind their backs, like students coming out of a lecture. As they passed in front of the paratroopers, they cast furtive glances towards them and lowered their voices. Finally, a small chap with fat rosy cheeks stopped in front of the paratroopers with a determined look and the others gathered round him. It was the first time they had had the opportunity to examine closely the camouflaged combat uniform and the Afrika

Korps-style cap, because the paratroopers had been brought directly to the wadi from their camp, and after the exercise Sergeant Marat had made them march some distance behind the platoon.

He was the last of the five, starting from the left, and he felt relaxed and comfortable with his back against the warm planks of the hut. The others were standing in front of him and looking at him with the expression of gentle envy that you see on the faces of soldiers in the brothels in Bône. They were doubtless thinking that in due course their rank would give them power over men just as simply as money supplied them with women to take to bed. But some of them looked rather like the type of little man at the Motor Show who looks at the big chromium-plated cars knowing very well that he'll end up with a Renault. They were the ones who knew that they would never be put in command of paratroops.

The cadet with the flabby cheeks smiled and said: 'Well, chaps, apparently you did a good job of work on the border . . . sounds as if you made sausage-meat of them . . .' He stopped for a reply but as no one answered he took a packet of 'Lucky Strike' out of the pocket of his dungarees, tapped it on the palm of his hand to loosen a few cigarettes, and held it out to the first paratrooper. He took three cigarettes, put one in his mouth, and placed one behind each ear; the next three did the same. When the packet reached him there were only two or three cigarettes left in it. He took the packet from the officer-cadet's hand and stuffed it in the left-hand pocket of his tunic, not so much for the cigarettes as not to disappoint the plump-cheeked cadet. And in fact, the latter smiled like someone who has successfully completed a demonstration and said: 'You really are tough, you lot!' Behind him, emerging from the solid group of officer-cadets, a voice shouted: 'They may be tough, but they're not funny.' Standing in the front row, an officer-cadet swung round like a robot: he was rather short, with a jutting jaw and steel-framed spectacles. 'No one wants them to be funny! Their job is just to be the best!' he flung back in his nasal voice. With his back to the wall, the heat from which he could feel on his back, the thought struck him that that cadet already had an officer's voice, a voice made to call over the roll of casualties. Then they moved aside to let Sergeant Marat

through, and speaking to his men as if he and they were entirely
on their own, he said quietly: 'Maoulen.' They got up and followed the sergeant in single file, their tommy-guns over their shoulders, quiet and sad like navvies going off to work.

*

Their captain with the pepper-and-salt hair had made a point of
climbing up into the truck with them instead of sitting beside the
driver. He had a Burgundian accent and he kept twisting his
heavy gold wedding-ring round his finger. He was trying to catch
Marat's eye in a friendly way but without success, because the
sergeant kept his eyes glued to the captain's decoration. There
were three bars dating from the Second War, but none to show
that he had spent any time in Indo-China. While the lorry drove
along the track leading to the wadi, the captain explained the
object of the exercise. This time the officer-cadets were going to
mount an operation against an ambush discovered by intelligence. Having been warned that the enemy had set a trap across
the wadi, they had to surprise and encircle them. Sergeant Marat
shook his head and said very quietly, hardly moving his lips: 'I'd
send out a light patrol, three or four bods, to advance slap-bang
into the ambush while I went quietly up each side of the wadi
with the others.' The captain stopped playing with his wedding-
ring. 'But you'd sacrifice your patrol,' he objected testily. 'Certainly. I'm not worried by a few casualties, if it helps me to kill
some wogs. While my four bods divert their attention and keep
them busy, I can attack and smash 'em up.' The captain was silent
for a minute, and then: 'What news of Amidouche?' Sergeant
Marat replied that it was a piece of cake and if Amidouche hadn't
existed he would have had to be invented. The regiment had been
brought back to rest at Zellifa after fighting on the Tunisian dam.
Thanks to Amidouche, they were keeping their hand in. They
were killing one or two wogs a week and this prevented them
from getting rusty. But the sergeant added that if Amidouche's
flea-bitten lot came across some easy game, they might do some
harm. The captain replied that they had telephoned to the
regimental C.P. before deciding to hold a night exercise. The
paratroops had located Amidouche's band on a djebel fifteen
kilometres or so away. They were going to try and round them

up that very evening. Marat said with a sigh that it was just his luck.

Night had fallen when the truck stopped by the bridge over the wadi. They jumped down on to the track and followed the captain in amongst the rocks. Walking cautiously and with a wary eye he led them as far as a gorge close to the spot where the exercise had taken place that afternoon. Here the wadi closed in, with steep banks on each side, covered with shrubs and cut by deep crevasses. The captain examined the terrain and then said, lowering his voice: 'Here we are. It seems just right to me.' 'Awaiting orders, captain,' Marat replied very loudly. The captain went on in a normal voice: 'Sergeant, you leave one man as an outpost in the bed of the wadi and take the others to establish a position on the slopes.' He took six magazines from his bag and handed them out to the paratroopers: 'Blank ammunition. That will get them used to gun-fire. Go ahead and load. I want to see you fix these magazines with my own eyes.' They took the magazines of live ammunition off their weapons and slipped them into their pockets, while Sergeant Marat drawled: 'Not to worry, captain. We'll treat them gently, your little boys . . .'

He was chosen to be the outpost. The captain took him forward fifty paces in front of the others and told him to conceal himself behind a rock. He added that it was only an exercise, after all, and that you mustn't discourage people who mean well and even if the outpost did detect the platoon when it was still a good way off, it would be a friendly act to pretend to be caught half off-guard. Then he gave him a tap on the shoulder and went off.

*

With his ear stuck to the ground, he heard them kicking stones under their feet when they were still a good thousand yards away. He stretched out on a strip of sand, with his LMG across his body and his hands behind his head. He would soon be hearing their weapons scraping against the rock. It was all obviously rather pointless but the officers probably wanted to accustom the platoon to operating at night.

The moon was not yet up: the sky above the wadi was almost as dark as the slopes of the gorge. There was not a breath of air. Now and again a prowling animal dislodged a stone. Throwing his head back, he could see the red dot of a paratrooper's cigarette It disappeared when a gun-barrel rang out against a rock, barely two hundred yards away.

He stood up and watched for them to approach, holding his gun at the hip. It was too dark to see their advance scouts but he soon located them by the sound. They were advancing very close together. When they were only a few yards away and he could hear them whispering, he pressed the trigger. At that precise moment the wadi was swept by a burst of automatic fire.

For two or three seconds, he was paralysed by surprise, and then he slid down beside the rock, slipped off the magazine of his machine-gun and replaced it by the magazine of live ammunition. It was Amidouche's machine-gun: the officers in the regiment didn't know exactly whether it was Yugoslav or Czech, but it shot faster than those used by the paratroopers. Its bullets were smacking against the rock and whining off as they ricocheted. It could not have been more than a hundred yards away, somewhere on the opposite ridge between the advance scouts and the main platoon.

He crawled round the rock and fired a short burst in what he estimated was the right direction. The firing opposite stopped. He heard the shrill voice of Sergeant Marat ordering them to withdraw. The machine-gun began firing again. Gathering himself together, in two leaps he reached the bank and dived into a sandy hollow. He immediately turned on his back, sensed a dark mass dominating him, and then a body crashed down onto him. He recognized an officer-cadet by the feel of his new dungarees. He broke loose and heard a clatter as men bolted down the slope. He just had time to pick up his tommy-gun and throw it away amongst the rocks before he was set upon and struck by a rifle-butt. Swaying, with red stars dancing in front of his eyes, he dimly felt his hands being tied behind his back. He kicked out with his right foot and hurled himself forward in the panic hope that they would finish him off on the spot. But they caught up with him and overpowered him. It was then he realized that they wanted him alive: a slow, spasmodic trembling started to run through his body, making his jaws chatter. He had seen the same sort of trembling in men who were being tortured by a magneto. The machine-gun had stopped firing but thirty or forty LMGs

271

were peppering away wildly on the right, where the platoon must be.

*

The two advance scouts had been captured with him. They were kept running for more than an hour with their hands tied behind their backs, surrounded by ten or so silent Arabs. The officer-cadets were out of breath and they kept on stumbling. When a halt was called at last, they collapsed on the ground, as if pole-axed. The moon was up. He saw that one of them was tall, fair-haired and slim; he was at least twenty-five; his mouth was open, his nose drawn tight, and he seemed to have difficulty in breathing. The second one was younger, of medium height, with a mop of black curly hair falling over his forehead. They had their eyes shut. Two of the Fells were having a whispered con-sultation. Finally, seven or eight of the Fells went off northwards and only two or three of them stayed behind to escort the prison-ers. They kicked the officer-cadets to their feet. They walked all night. The leading Fell quickened the pace still more when the sky began to grow paler in the east. At dawn, they stopped on the brow of a hill dotted with bushes and lay down in the thickest clump. He went to sleep almost immediately.

Towards eleven o'clock in the morning, he was awakened by the heat and perhaps also by loud voices. The officer-cadets had been untied and were sitting beside him with two Fells. The third one, twenty yards or so away, was keeping watch on the horizon with his hand shielding his eyes.

He sat up and rubbed his numbed arms; the cord was biting into his wrists, his throat was parched, and his tongue felt like a piece of rough wood. The two Fells were looking at him and smiling. They were oldish, at least thirty and dressed in French army dungarees similar to those of the officer-cadets. They were wearing new desert boots. They were both holding in their hands, like a deck of cards, a number of photos, some of them in colour. It was probably the slim, fair-haired cadet who had handed them over to them; his wallet was open on his lap. The Fell who was almost bald said, still smiling, how very pleased they were to have hit the jack-pot, because they hadn't expected to pick a para-trooper. The fair-haired prisoner smiled as well and put out his

272

hand for the photos. The second Fell handed back the ones that he was holding, saying that he had a very nice-looking fiancée and that he should have brought her with him to Algeria. The prisoner gave a laugh and put his wallet back into his pocket. Then he asked: 'What do you do to the paratroopers that you capture alive?' As the Fells didn't reply, he went on: 'Do you know, believe it or not, I feel closer to you than to those swine. We chaps all belong to the people, don't we, and we ought to get together over their heads instead of smashing each other up!' He explained that he was a school-master, and as a left-winger he was a militant supporter of the freedom of nations. He spoke at length about a manifesto in favour of peace in Algeria which he had circulated amongst his colleagues, and which had earned him a warning from the senior inspector of schools. The Fells asked what a manifesto was; he explained it to them. Then the bald Fell asked the second officer-cadet if he had any photos to show too. He replied no, he was an orphan, and he went very red when the Fell said to him that he must have a photo of his bird. The school-master pointed out that his comrade was studying for the priesthood. The Fells burst out laughing: the bald one said that they were always surprised to see a priest in the army. The seminarist explained that he had decided long ago not to kill or wound his neighbour; he would fire into the air. The other Fell, who was small and very lean, thought for a few seconds, wrinkling his forehead, and then exclaimed, slapping his thigh, that it was quite clever of him to have decided to be an officer: like that he wouldn't be obliged to kill anyone himself – all he would need to do would be to give the orders to shoot. The seminarist shook his head and said that he didn't mean it like that, he hadn't understood. The schoolmaster went on, speaking in a strained voice: 'Listen, you're wrong if you think that we're just trying to save our skins. I don't mind getting bumped off but at least I want it to serve some good purpose. I'd hate to be killed serving a handful of lousy settlers and Fascist generals. I'll tell you frankly, if you take me with you, I'll consider it an honour and I swear I'd do a good job for you. I wouldn't mind shooting my neighbour down if my neighbour was a swine.' The Fell said it was rather like Italy in '43 when there were good Italians and bad Italians, that you didn't quite know what was happening, it was a real headache. He picked up a goatskin water-bottle and took a drink. The other Fell followed suit and then passed the goatskin to the school-master. He watched them drink, and he could feel a fire smouldering in his throat. The school-master took several deep swallows, staring him straight in the eyes. When the seminarist had also finished drinking, he hesitated a moment before handing the drinking bottle back to the little Fell. With his tongue sticking to his parched palate, he looked at the bald Fell and wondered where and when he had seen him before.

At about two o'clock, out of the blue, a young lad suddenly made his appearance amongst them. Nobody had seen him come. He ran over to the Fell who was keeping watch and shouted a few sentences before disappearing again. The Fell came down towards them looking worried. He was about twenty and was wearing a faded khaki shirt, blue jeans and very worn canvas shoes. He signalled that they must leave.

Half an hour later, as they were moving rapidly across a rocky plateau, they heard the shrill whistling sound of a helicopter coming up behind them. The Fells quickened their pace. He fell down twice, hampered in his running by his wrists, which were still bound together. The officer-cadets had their hands free and could keep up without difficulty.

The plateau came to an abrupt end in a sharp cliff which fell sheer a good three hundred feet down to the dried-up bed of a wadi; on the other side, the ground rose in a gentle slope up to a bare mound. A patrol of paratroopers was scrambling down the slope.

The Fells made them lie down at the extreme edge of the plateau, where a few bushes were growing. The Fell in blue jeans flopped down on his right and stuffed a dirty rag in his mouth which squashed his tongue right back against his palate. The pain made him shut his eyes, but he opened them almost at once as he felt a prick on the right side of his neck. The Fell had got a knife in his hand, ready to cut his throat. Raising his head a little, he saw the paratroopers. There were nine of them, in single file. In the middle of the column he recognized Sergeant Marat, well set-up in his combat uniform which he had had altered to fit more snugly over his thighs and shoulders. Even at that distance, the sergeant's nervousness was plain to see; his head was moving incessantly from right to left as if he was watching a tennis-match and he was holding his LMG at hip-level, ready to fire. Sergeant Marat had joined the company just before embarking for Algeria. He had told them all about Indo-China during the crossing. According to him, after having lived through Dien-Bien-Phu, only war with Russia would be really interesting; he spoke with bored contempt of what they might expect in the djebels. By the time they had arrived in Bône they knew the meaning of all the Vietnamese words with which he studded his conversation. They used him for the quiet jobs; the captain had chosen him immediately to lead the group simulating the enemy in the officer-cadets' exercise.

When the paratroopers were only about a hundred yards from the wadi, the Fell forced him to put his head down. With his right cheek digging into the dust, his face was quite close to that of the school-master lying to the left of him. With his mouth half-open and his eyes closed, the school-master seemed in a paralytic trance; his features were fixed in a kind of pleading desperation.

The helicopter passed very low overhead; the movement of air made the bushes sway. Its engine was idling; no doubt it was going to land somewhere on the right. They heard Sergeant Marat shout: 'Maoulen! Maoulen!' At the bottom of the wadi there was a sound of pounding feet which quickly died away. The school-master's lower lip started trembling; his face lost its strained look and seemed to fall apart with disappointment. The helicopter's engine continued to idle for ten minutes or so, and then opened up. It must have been taking off quite close, because they could feel the swirl of warm air from its rotor blades. The Fells waited for it to disappear southwards before getting up; they looked at each other, smiling.

He got up too. The Fell in blue jeans pulled his gag out. He felt that he would never manage to free his tongue from the back of his palate. His facial contortions made the Fell laugh. He unhooked the water-bottle from his belt and dropped it on the ground. Tied as he was, in order to drink he would have had to squat down, catch hold of the gourd between his knees and unscrew the stopper with his teeth. With a kick he sent it flying ten yards away. The Fell was watching him closely, with a patient

275

look on his face, as if his prisoner was setting him a slightly difficult problem which he nevertheless was quite sure of being able to solve. The school-master went and picked up the water-bottle, and gave it back to the Fell saying 'You're too kind to those swine. If you knew what they say about you!' The curly black-haired young seminarist had moved a few paces away and was looking towards the south. He gave a jump when the bald Fell rammed the barrel of his gun into the small of his back. 'Priest,' shouted the Fell, 'you prayed just now for your friends to discover us!' The seminarist looked completely desperate and stammered a denial but the Fell insisted that he had seen his lips moving. The seminarist looked at the school-master and whispered: 'What are they going to do with us?' The other shrugged his shoulders and said: 'They can't do us any harm, they know that we're on their side.' The bald Fell slapped him on the shoulder and said: 'Yes, you're good chaps.' The school-master relaxed completely and he continued to chat with the bald Fell, giving only a casual glance at the Fell in the blue jeans who now gave the order to move on.

In his opinion, the school-master was mistaken in looking on the Fell as a negligible quantity. He was younger and less well-dressed but he was certainly an old member of Amidouche's band; the others must have been enrolled only two or three months ago. He could remember having seen the bald Fell before: it was in an Arab café in Zellifa where he was a waiter. He had disappeared at the same time as a dozen others; they had a pretty good idea where they had gone to. Amidouche had organized his operation nicely. First of all he had let himself be located with his band fifteen kilometres from the training ground, thus drawing off the paratroopers. Against the cadets, he had sent in his new recruits with a few old hands to lead them. After the ambush, the main body of his troops had moved away northwards to create a diversion while the three Fells and their prisoners were marching westwards towards the djebels. The officers considered that area as more free from rebels than the others; that was why they had sent Sergeant Marat there.

So Amidouche wanted some prisoners. He had the reputation of being a cool customer who would not do anything without a purpose. If he had taken so many risks to pick up two men from the cadet platoon, it was so that one morning in the near future the officer-cadets would find the mutilated corpses of the school-master and the seminarist at the entrance to their camp. Usually, Amidouche didn't torture small fry: he just had their throats slit. But like all the Fells, he knew that a few dead bodies, suitably worked-on, can break the morale of a still untried unit. That would mean an unpleasant death for the school-master and the seminarist.

As for him, being a parachutist he knew what his lot would be: first tortured and then impaled; this was the invariable rule.

*

At dusk they halted. The Fells shared a few dried figs and cheese with the officer-cadets. The worst thing was when they took hold of the water skins, threw their heads back and swallowed the water in large gulps. Everyone was tired and ate in silence. When they had finished chewing, the two Fells in dungarees looked at the younger one with a querying look. He thought for a few seconds before nodding yes. The bald Fell leapt up and walked towards where he was sitting a little to one side, next to the young Fell. But the latter shook his head and smiled, as he put his hand on his prisoner's shoulder to show that that one belonged to him. The bald Fell hesitated a moment and then ordered the school-master to get up; the third Fell took hold of the seminarist by the hair and pulled him to his feet. The bald Fell went off with the school-master to the left while the other one took the seminarist away to the right.

Night had come but the moon had risen and the young Fell's face could be seen quite plainly. Squatting on his heels he was smoking a cigarette held in the hollow of his hand to hide the glow. He was rather good-looking, with black hair, a hooked nose and full lips; his eyes had a calm and serious expression. Suddenly he lifted his head and called out to remind them not to forget to tie their arms and legs for the night.

The school-master was the first to cry out. They heard him screaming oaths and insults and then there was a silence marked by a dull thud that might have been a blow from a rifle-butt; after that the school-master confined himself to pleading. More than anger or pain, his voice revealed immense surprise. The

277

seminarist who was sobbing without protesting seemed surprised too; now and again he stopped crying and then began again in a tone of outraged and bewildered incredulity. The thought crossed his mind that they didn't know that Amidouche forbade his men to touch the women in the villages they went through; they had to make do as best they could.

Keeping his eyes fixed on the young Fell, he let himself fall backwards with his right leg extended sideways, his left leg bent, arching his back. The Fell frowned and looked surprised; then with a half smile on his lips he crawled over to him on his hands and knees and unbuckled the belt of his camouflage trousers. He raised himself to release his trousers and pants and the Fell pulled them down to his ankles. Then, of his own accord, he turned over and waited, arching his back. He felt the Fell straddle him and heard him give a surprised, slightly contemptuous chuckle of pleasure; and as he imagined to himself what the Fell was seeing and feeling he could understand that chuckle. The school-master had at least stopped pleading, and now, like the seminarist, he was crying, but on a deeper note. The Fell stretched himself out completely. As the tied hands were getting in his way he undid them, and turning him over rather roughly tied them again, this time in front. He got in position again and heard the Fell clear his throat and spit; he felt his thumb pressing into the saliva. Then, feeling something warm pushing against him, he moved his hips to guide it. Clenching his teeth in order not to cry out he submitted to this unbelievable, unprecedented intrusion at the centre of his body. When he could move to and fro freely, the Fell stopped for a moment. He felt his hair being grasped; slowly and forcibly the Fell rubbed his face against the ground. Then the hands felt his cheeks, his nose, his lips as if wanting to take possession of them. He didn't resist but, on the contrary, became as flexible and docile as he could. Then a hand penetrated into his mouth and fingers furtively brushed against his teeth; he guessed that they were afraid of being bitten and he licked them, his tongue picking up the grit that had been caught under the nails. Then the Fell gave a moan and rammed home.

When it was over he remained lying on him, inert, for quite a long while before rolling over sideways; taking a piece of cord out of his satchel, he tied his legs; and then pulled up his blue

278

jeans, closed the zip and, with a sigh, subsided onto his back with arms outstretched. Watchfully, he observed the now relaxed, peaceful face and half-closed eyes. As he had hoped, the Fell had omitted to bind his arms behind his back again. He crept closer to him, rested his head on his chest and, very gently, slid it under his chin with his lips touching his throat. The Fell gave a little smile and casually stroked the back of his head. They stayed like this for several minutes and he could feel the body of the young Fell drowsy but not really quite dropping off to sleep. Then he decided to try sudden force. He rolled sideways, grasped the boulder that he'd spotted with both hands and swinging back like a pendulum smashed it down onto the Fell's forehead where it joined the left temple: he heard a bone crack. He struck five times more and then stopped, breathless, his hands sticky with blood. Then he took the Fell's knife out of its sheath and cut the cord binding his ankles; to cut his wrists free he gripped the knife-handle between his knees and ran the cord over the edge of the blade. Next he unzipped the blue jeans and cut off the penis – it was like cutting through rubber; he carefully placed the penis in the Fell's wide-open mouth. While he was arranging his clothes, which took a few seconds, he looked at him; only then did he take the water-bottle, unscrew the stopper and drink deeply. He also picked up the Fell's rifle, looked towards where the moans and crying had been coming from a short while ago, then turned and went away.

Date: 6.6.1968   Classification: TS
From: Minerva   Ref. no. 2120 RD
To: Mercury
Subject: Operation Régis

Sarah Roboul will be allotted the identification no. 51A.

8848 is to remain in contact with 51A. He will endeavour to turn his association with 51A into a stable relationship. He will represent himself as a strong supporter of 51A's political opinions, at the same time concealing his particular methods of putting them into practice. The intention is to lead 51A to deduce, of her own accord, that he is engaged in underground revolutionary activity. In view of 51A's romantic activist leanings, this result should not be difficult to achieve.

The operation will be allotted the code-word Régis.

We take note of the reservations concerning 8848 expressed in your memo 2117 BP of 6.6.1968.

Date: 13.6.1968   Classification: TS
From: Mercury   Ref. no. 2121 LK
To: Minerva
Subject: DL 51

In our memo 2079 WB of 23.4.1968 we informed you of our
identification, thanks to 55, of Simone Derelle, secretary, residing
at 18 Rue du Cardinal Lemoine, Paris V.

Approach to the subject was delayed by the fact that she left
Paris at the time of the recent events. In her absence, 8425 undertook preliminary enquiries with her neighbours and tradesmen,
posing as an inspector of a credit firm. The results were nil
because the subject keeps to herself, talks to no one and her
disagreeable character arouses general antipathy.

On 7.6.1968, 8425 telephoned to the subject at her office
(International Paper Works, 96 Rue Bleue, Paris IX) on the
pretext of conducting a public opinion survey. He informed the
subject that she had been selected as a sample for a political
opinion poll, and asked her whether she would agree to reply to
a questionnaire. On receiving an affirmative reply, he arranged
to meet the subject at her home that very day.

8425 called at 18 Rue du Cardinal Lemoine at about 1900 hrs.
The subject immediately asked him to prove that he belonged to
the above-mentioned public opinion survey organization. 8425
presented his card. The subject took it from him and rang up a
person with whom she seemed on friendly terms. From the
ensuing conversation, 8425 realized:

1) that the person rung up by the subject was a senior official
in the public opinion poll organization;

2) that the subject had rung him up earlier in the afternoon to
enquire whether it was he who had had her selected as a sample;

281

3) that he had replied in the negative;

4) that when he had checked that the subject's name did not appear on any sample lists, the subject had promised to call him back during 8425's visit.

When the subject hung up saying: 'I'll wait for you', 8425 stated that he was a life-insurance agent and that his previous misrepresentations had been a subterfuge intended to facilitate his approach to prospective clients. As the subject refused to return his card, 8425 snatched it from her and left the flat.

We instruct Socrates *as a matter of extreme urgency to* arrange for 8425 to leave France immediately. Any investigation of the subject is to be halted until further notice. We have informed Hecate verbally of what has happened. Hecate intends to issue a general circular banning the adoption of the identity of public opinion pollsters until further orders.

Date: 18.6.1968   Classification: TS
From: Mercury   Ref. no. 2122 EW
To: Minerva
Subject: DL 51

Dead Leaves XII

Herewith typescript of relevant part of a recorded conversation between 8047 and Jean-François Brauchite, commercial traveller, residing at 89 Rue Guillaume, Flers (Orne).

Contact was made at the subject's house on 7.6.1968.

8047 was under the assumed cover of a life-assurance agent.

The subject is thirty-two years old. He has two children. His wife Nicole is pregnant.

1 enclosure

Brauchite — in the negative my dear sir, definitely in the negative/ that sort of thing gives me a pain in the arse/nothing happened here at Flers but I don't mind telling you that if those little shysters had tried anything on they'd've got the shock of their precious little lives/I was in the war you know/real war not a little scuffle with the fuzz who when they get hit on the head with a brickbat just sit up and beg for more/I've killed fells my dear sir I served as an officer in the black berets fifth regiment so you see I can't take your squawking little brats seriously/I've got a good remedy for little twits like that anyway a nice quick injection of point 38 and they'd be as quiet as mice/ yes just like those little oas bastards who looked so pleased with themselves on the terrace of the automatic well after the rue d'isly there were forty wogs lying on the deck pht and after that no more trouble/believe me if the police had only had the guts to let 'em have it they'd all be sitting their exams now whether they liked it or not.

8047 — I'm sure there's a lot of truth in what you're saying/ when were you in Algeria/myself I left in 58/just before 13th May

B — 58/you were a regular then/I say that because of your age

8047 — I was recalled/we were in the oran area on the

284

moroccan border

B   – the constantinois/nice part/who was it who had to take on the katibas who were skipping over from tunisia/the good old fifth/always ready when there was a tough job/we really copped a packet at la grotte du juif no connection with my lady's grotto/ you should have seen it

8047   – so you became an officer after call-up

B   – yes officer-training course july 56 at cherchell/I got my stripe straightaway/we had a queer course of instruction though/the week we arrived the fells clashed with a whole infantry company/all over in double quick time/cross machine-gun fire a quick defensive mopping up/a dozen pbi on the deck and forty prisoners we found them afterwards with a beautiful berber smile across their throats/I don't mind telling you that it gave us quite a turn

8047   – but I remember that business/cherchell 56 somebody was mentioning it to me only recently

B   – perhaps you read a thing about it somewhere apparently there's an egg-head who's produced a book about the fells in which he talks about that clash and blames us for having left prisoners/what a hope/although it's true that the fifth would never have left anyone alive to fall into their hands

8047   – no that wasn't it/I didn't read it/it was one of my clients who mentioned it to me/just a sec/yes auphal was the name dominique auphal

B   – auphal/well now isn't the world a small place – auphal I was with him at cherchell/what's become of old auphal

8047   – well he's doing very well/he's married and he's got children and he's got a sense of his responsibilities he's taken out a life assurance policy

B   – you don't miss any chances do you/ok I understand after all we're really doing the same sort of job aren't we/whether it's an adding machine or an insurance policy we've got to sell our goods/dear old auphal that's fantastic/did he tell you how he nearly bumped me off cleaning his mat/no I'm not surprised/they hushed it up nobody ever heard anything about it otherwise it would have been goodbye to his commission/bloody old auphal/or the time he saved the skin of a fell/the stupid bugger was an advance scout/a night exercise/he heard something moving in the bushes/not to worry he said after taking a decko it's some sort of animal it's gone now/you bet he confessed to me afterwards that he'd seen an ayrab tucked up asleep and he hadn't had the heart to let him have it in cold blood/you see that was typical of auphal/there was nobody quite like him for hair-splitting/you know have we the right to kill and is our war a fair war and shouldn't we really be with the chaps on the other side/nice bloke in spite of that but always wondering whether you ought to tickle it with the little finger or shove your thumb right up/always snivelling over the arabs/and the same for the settlers/if he went out to dinner with a pied noir by the time the dessert arrived there he was talking about the africans/you know he used to say to me they've got their dead buried here too/as for me to be honest my chief worry was not to finish up alongside them/now it's at the time of the oas that old auphal would've been in his element he'd've liked that little game of swings and roundabouts/in the morning on the side of the fells and in the evening on the side of the pieds noirs yes he couldn't have resisted that temptation/you're lucky he used to say you're not worried by problems /he can say that again/but I don't like other people setting me problems either/if the fells shoot me in the arse tac tac tac tac/if the pieds noirs start using plastic on me tac tac tac tac/and just bring cohn-bendit along tac tac tac tac/is that fair or not

8047   — there's certainly a lot of truth in it

B   — you're like me eh the customer is always right/oh yes I know that tune too/to come back to business I'll tell you what we'll do we'll ask nicole that's my wife and we'll see what she thinks/after all she's the person most interested/nicole/nicole get out the arsenic there's a gentleman here who's offering you a great thick wad of notes if you can manage to bump me off

(ends)

Following our memo 2060 MW of 20.3.1968 concerning an
unauthorized approach by a member of the Aesculapius section
to Minerva 3 and subsequent contact between them a special
enquiry was instigated by you.

In the interests of a current operation, we should be glad to
hear what conclusions of any sort you may have reached on this
matter up to the present.

Date: 21.6.1968
From: Mercury
To: Minerva
Subject: DL 51

Classification: TS
Ref. no. 2124 VK

Dead Leaves XIII

1) The Lindbergh material has enabled us to locate Jean Poulignon, formerly in charge of the J.E.C. at Collège Ladislas, author of a letter addressed to 51 on 20.6.1944 (ref. no. 2097 ZQ) at present residing at 50 Rue Maurice Ravel, Paris XII, managing director of the publishing firm 'Editions Chrétiennes' of 14 Rue Manin, Paris XIX. Ways of approaching the above are being explored.

2) It has not proved possible to locate Michel Delille, author of a letter addressed to 51 on 14.6.1944 (ref. no. 2097 GF). Enquiry at the address given on the above letter (Mme Lenpetit, Rue de la Nation, Balbigny) proved fruitless, as the house has been pulled down and its occupants have moved to an unknown address.

3) It has not proved possible to identify the author of a letter signed 'Veau Académique' addressed to 51 on 29.12.1946 (ref. no. 2098 KH). The information provided in para. 2 of Appendix IV of the Lindbergh material (ref. no. 2090 DB) has however enabled us to locate Bernard de Cantricourt, engineer, residing at 3 Avenue de Maréchal Foch, Meudon (Haute-de-Seine), who was a scout at the same time as 51 (34th Paris Troop, section Cardinal Dubois, Vaugirard district). 8653 telephoned the subject, under the cover of an employee at French Scout Headquarters. The subject stated that he had never known 51 very well, since the latter belonged to the Chamois Patrol, whereas the subject was a member of the Reindeer Patrol. He remembers him as being an introverted and unstable boy. 51's totem was

'Melancholy Kitten'. The subject informed 8653 that 51 had a friend in the Chamois patrol called Daniel Salairons who might be able to give more exact information about 51. Enquiries are in hand to attempt to locate Daniel Salairons.

Date: 24.6.1968   Classification: TS
From: Mercury   Ref. no. 2125 TC
To: Minerva
Subject: DL 51

At our request Apollo went into the question of the work
mentioned by Jean-François Brauchite in the course of his conversation with 8047 (v. DL XII, ref. no. 2122 Ew).

The book is 'Histoire du F.L.N.' by Jacques C. Duchemin,
published in September 1962 by the Table Ronde, 40 Rue du
Bac, Paris VII.

We enclose an extract from Chapter II, pp. 124-126.

1 enclosure

Dead Leaves XIV

During the time when Si Mohammed was commanding the IVth Wilaya, a young political R.S.M. sector leader, Ahmed Z . . . by name, who later went over to the French, was in charge of a regional commando which successfully ambushed a service company of the Cherchell Officers' Training School as it was on its way to a new location. Twelve soldiers were killed and four taken prisoner. As neither paratroopers, marines nor 'chasseurs alpins' were involved, Ahmed Z . . . felt sure that the survivors would make good their escape without carrying off their dead and wounded with them and this they in fact did.

The F.L.N. were thus able to avail themselves of Colonel Ben Tobbal's Standing Order No. 2a recommending that corpses should always be systematically mutilated and they castrated the unfortunate troops killed in the ambush. While Ben Tobbal intended this as a deliberate measure of intimidation against newly conscripted troops and an important element in a general terror campaign, the members of the commando looked on it merely as a cruel form of fun, although an officially authorized one. But we can let Ahmed Z . . . tell the story in the words he himself used during an interrogation conducted after he had deserted to the French.

'The four prisoners were pretty demoralized; we made them come along with us with the help of a few kicks up the behind but without subjecting them to any really rough treatment. It wasn't until that evening after supper that we tied their wrists together. The first night we slept in a mechta in B . . . village.

'Next day we played poker with them. They were very pleasant with us and I think that they were beginning to feel reassured. The second evening our liaison man returned and told us that the colonel did not want us to take any prisoners with us. As a result we had a discussion and each of us chose our man for that night. As I was in charge, I took Sergeant X... from Angers. I remember that he had freckles.

'Beforehand, I took his papers and read his letters to his fiancée. I also looked at the photos of his fiancée. He didn't offer any resistance because I think he hoped that this might save his life. I didn't dare to tell him that he was going to be killed next day. Afterwards I undid his hands and we smoked a French cigarette from an army issue packet that he had on him and that we had allowed him to keep.

'The other three didn't offer any resistance either as far as I could hear, but one of them did cry, the one who had been taken by Omar. Next day, we told them that we had to go to the medical centre. We made them sit on the ground with their hands tied. They all seemed quite relaxed but when they saw us whispering they began to suspect something.

'We took them away one by one, and before cutting their throats we knocked them unconscious with a stone. They cried out a little while they were being taken away, but they didn't suffer. They said that they wanted to stay with us and would fight with us if we didn't kill them. We took their clothes off for our own use but without touching their bodies. I took the papers and photos and kept them.'

'Why did you subject those soldiers to physical abuse before killing them?'

'We didn't have any women, we were just like animals.'

1) Since the special measures adopted to deal with Aesculapius
19 had been ordered by myself, Hecate was, strictly speaking,
debarred from passing on to you any information relating
thereto. Notwithstanding this, I see no reason to delay in informing you that I have definitely decided to dismiss Aesculapius 19,
whatever conclusions Hecate may have reached in the report
which is being submitted to me shortly. In any event Aesculapius
19 represents a security risk that I cannot allow to continue.

2) I have been giving consideration to your suggestion concerning Hervé Bérasse. This suggestion interests me, and if the
financing of his paper can be kept within reasonable limits, it
would seem certain that this financial control would enable us
to place one or two agents who, on journalistic grounds, would
have excellent opportunities of moving about freely and conducting investigations, above all when it is remembered that the
periodical is to be concerned with tourism. I shall put Bérasse
into Hecate's hands. If he receives clearance from them I shall
pass the practical details of the negotiations over to Apollo who
will report results to you direct.

Date: 26.6.1968
From: Minerva
To: Aesculapius
Subject: 51

Classification: TS
Ref. no. 2126 IT

Herewith the relevant portions of the dossier on 51, i.e. the documents under the following ref. nos:–

1978 PD	2002 VP	2076 MA
1979 AV	(+ 1 photo)	2077 VC
1980 UC	2003 VA	2078 TK
1981 GG	(+ 5 photos)	2079 WB
1982 CN	2007 VA	2080 DK
1983 UG	2008 ZV	2081 CP
1984 KV	2011 BG	2082 KZ
1985 FF	2012 GG	2083 DC
1986 MD	2013 IK	2084 BZ
1986 Md	2016 GD	2085 SV
1990 GP	2019 DM	2086 GB
1992 ZQ	2020 VA	2087 KC
1993 TR	2021 JO	2088 MO
1994 ZA	2024 VL	2090 DB
1995 OV	(+ 12 photos)	2091 BP
1996 MO	2038 MM	2092 QM
1997 PT	2063 DM	2093 ZZ
1998 JP	2064 RG	2094 KE
1999 HN	2070 WA	2095 CV
2000 TG	2072 QP	2096 KD
2001 UR	2074 KG	2097 GF
(+ 1 photo)	2075 EP	2097 ZQ

2098 KH	2111 IR	2121 LK
2100 HM	2113 LC	2122 EW
2105 DN	2115 TS	2122 Ew
2106 RA	2117 BP	2124 VK
2107 BJ	2118 BR	2125 TC
2109 VC	2119 CU	2125 Tc
2110 MN	2120 RD	

Principal persons involved:

51:	The objective
51A:	51's former mistress
52:	51's wife
52A:	52's former lover
53:	51's and 52's son
54:	51's and 52's daughter
55:	51's and 52's former servant
56:	51's secretary

This dossier has already been communicated to you in part (v. your memo 2036 BA of 3.1.1968). Your diagnosis was, negative (v. your report no. 2048 BB of 12.2.1968).

We rely entirely on your competence in examining and interpreting this file. Purely for your guidance as laid down in standing orders, we put forward the following working hypothesis:

51's affections seem polarized round his children and in particular round 53. His feelings towards 52 are not strong. There is a strong possibility that his sexual activity is limited. The file shows that the only person towards whom 51 has ever had feelings of a passionate nature is 51A. The problem is to discover if those feelings still persist and if so whether they persist at least in part as strongly as they did earlier. Two facts seem to point to an affirmative answer to this question:

1) 51 keeps a photograph of 51A in his wallet.

2) When he met 51A recently he assured her that he regretted that they had parted.

It appears both from 51A's evidence and from the posthumous letter of 51's mother that 51 parted from 51A as a result of a guilt complex vis-à-vis his putative father.

It is a fact that 51A has retained 'at least a real feeling of tenderness' for 51.

We envisage the possibility of reactivating the relationship between 51 and 51A. Such a reactivation, which is in any case tacitly desired by both parties, might well be engineered by making 51 aware, by means that are yet to be devised, where his true sympathies lie.

If this hypothesis is confirmed by your diagnosis, we would take steps on our side for the appropriate exploitation of the objective. We would stress that there would be no question of subjecting 51 to objective pressure on the part of 51A with a view to encouraging him to co-operate willingly. We rather envisage manipulating 51A in such a way as to get her to exploit 51 without him being aware of it. 51A's romantic activist leanings and her experiences of underground activity seem suitable for this sort of exploitation. Properly handled, 51A might well be able to reconcile her feelings towards 51 with activities that she would consider as furthering her own extremist views.

Date: 28.6.1968
From: Mercury
To: Minerva
Subject: Opération Régis

Classification: TS
Ref. no. 2127 CC

8848 reports that he has lost contact with 51A since 6.6.1968 on which date he had a short conversation with her on the subject of the political situation in France.

51A has not returned to her home since 10.6.1968.

On 13.6.1968 at 1700 hrs her premises were searched by French security forces (D.S.T.).

51A's disappearance and the searching of her premises could be explained by the fact that she belongs to one of the political organizations recently dissolved by French government decree.

We have urgently ordered 8848 to cease Opération Régis forthwith. The risks implied by the intervention of the D.S.T. who already showed interest in the subject some years ago exclude to our mind any hope of pursuing this operation further, even as a long-term proposition.

Date: 1.7.1968   Classification: TS
From: Mercury   Ref. no. 2128 RC
To: Minerva
Subject: DL 51

5672 reports that 52 has engaged a servant to replace 5354.

This servant is a woman of Mediterranean type, about thirty years of age. She speaks French with a strong Spanish accent.

5672 is endeavouring to discover her identity.

Date: 5.7.1968
From: Mercury
To: Minerva
Subject: DL 51

Classification: TS
Ref. no. 2129 TJ

8956 reports that 55 left his home on 26.6.1968, removing her personal effects with her.

In accordance with the instructions contained in your memo 2107 BJ of 9.5.1968, 8956 had asked 55 to introduce him to her parents. 8956 and 55 went to Maupertain on 8.6.1968. 55's parents made him relatively welcome as a result of 8956's apparent standard of living. It was decided to make an official announcement of the engagement subject to the agreement of 52's parents, where 55's father is employed in the stables. On 8956's advice, 55 wrote to 51 and 52 announcing her impending marriage and apologizing for her abrupt departure. No reply was received to this letter, which was despatched on 11.6.1968. It had been agreed between 8956 and 55 that they would go back to Maupertain again on 14.7.1968 to call on 52's parents.

According to 8956, since their visit to 55's parents, 55 had seemed noticeably less concerned about their marriage. His view was that the steps that either had been or were going to be taken had reassured her as to her future. 55's sudden unexplained disappearance has made him wonder whether this change of attitude did not have another reason. He does not exclude the possibility that 55 may have met another man.

We have asked 5672 to keep watch on 51's and 52's house on the unlikely assumption that 55 may return to Delphi.

Date: 8.7.1968
From: Mercury
To: Minerva
Subject: DL 51

Classification: TS
Ref. no. 2130 SA

The Lindbergh material has enabled us to identify Jean Poulignon, formerly in charge of the J.E.C. at the Collège Ladislas, author of a letter sent to 51 on 20.6.1944 (ref. no. 2097 ZQ), at present residing at 50 Rue Maurice Ravel, Paris XII, and managing director of the publishing firm 'Editions Chrétiennes', 14 Rue Manin, Paris XIX.

In view of our knowledge of the subject's particular characteristics, Cleitos was directed to make the approach.

As a result of a preliminary contact by telephone, the subject wrote Cleitos the enclosed letter.

1 enclosure

Dead Leaves XV

Paris, 29th June 1968

Reverend Father,

As I mentioned on the telephone yesterday, it is many years since I last saw Dominique Auphal. He was one of my junior J.E.C. members at Ladislas during the years immediately following the Liberation. He is a boy whom I have never forgotten, for reasons which I shall explain. You must have thought me rather reticent on the phone. I must confess that it was a purely instinctive reaction. I realized it myself and that is why I asked for time to think before giving you any reply. The question you asked me was important and I owe it to my conscience to weigh my words carefully.

You told me that he has become a high-level civil servant, a fact of which I was unaware – indeed I do not know what has become of most of my boys. Moreover Dominique had ceased being a member of the J.E.C. before he left Ladislas as a result of a very unfortunate incident. I'm afraid that I can't remember the exact date. At that time, I was keeping a diary which I have since mislaid. It must have been around '46 or '47 and Dominique would have been fifteen or sixteen. Before breaking up for Easter, we had asked our juniors to do something special for Lord Jesus during their holidays and to write a report. I have always believed in the virtue of meditation after action. It is good to do something, but it is even better to think about what you have done because you can then see better what you could have done and what needs to be done. We agreed that we should

302

look at the reports together at the beginning of term and see what lessons we could draw from them. I hardly need to tell you what those young lads told us: that they had helped their mother to look after their younger brothers or sisters, run errands for an elderly neighbour, and so on. The act was less important than the intention. Dominique's report quite amazed us (I say us because I was working in charge of the section in conjunction with Bertrand Fléchart who was preparing for Saint-Cyr and who was later to die very gallantly in Indo-China). It was the longest report of them all and I must admit that it was very well written. It was a day-to-day diary. Dominique told the story of his first meeting with a boy who, like himself, was holidaying at Senlis (I seem to remember that Dominique was spending Easter with his grandparents or with friends of his parents, I can't remember exactly and it's not important). This boy had lost his faith after a serious moral crisis, the ostensible reason for which I've forgotten (it may have been the sudden death of his father or mother). Whatever the pretext, he had ceased to believe and had even taken to preaching atheism to his school-fellows (he was at a state school). Dominique's diary gave an account of his conversation with the boy, their theological discussions, rather elementary but quite touching, and his efforts to bring this lost sheep back to the fold. I can assure you that it was most remarkable. Bertrand and I were indeed moved to the depths of our souls. The end was especially moving, because it was Easter Sunday and it was on that very day of glory that Dominique and his friend, who had been touched by grace and reconciled with God, knelt down side by side for Holy Eucharist. This account of an authentic conversion made Bertrand and myself somewhat lose our heads, I fear. We read the report out loud to the whole section and everyone was open-mouthed with wonder. All of us (and Bertrand and I were amongst the first) sat looking at Dominique with awe and envy and the little blackguard sat there blushing with his eyes downcast. As you can see, even twenty years on, the memory of our foolishness puts words into my mouth that I must beg you to forgive. Our first reaction later on was perhaps too harsh, indeed it certainly must have been, but Father Descozes, who quickly succeeded in getting Dominique to admit his fraud (he had invented the whole story from beginning to end!), must share some of the responsibility, because he poked so much fun at us that we were led to forget the virtue of charity. We should have tried to understand before condemning. I must confess that first of all I suspected him of wanting to show off. But Dominique was a queer, insecure boy who was afraid of not fitting in with the others. Basically, he had great difficulty in communicating. I think that in fact it was because of his feeling of insecurity that he had invented this story of a conversion. He would have thought that after such a remarkable feat as that he would be accepted once and for all by the section. My later experience showed me that adolescents often behaved like that in moments of stress: they 'put on side' more through weakness than because they want to show off. We think that they want to be superior and that is irritating, whereas in fact all they want to do is to be accepted. These poor young lads are merely trying to find a niche for themselves which is not necessarily a prominent one at all.

I haven't seen Dominique since and I have made no attempt to do so, although I should have tried and then welcomed him with a friendly, outstretched hand. I confess that it was fear of what other people might think that held me back and I feel obliged to admit that this stupid affair of conversion is one of my most unpleasant memories.

That is all I can tell you. I'm glad to know that he is married and has children, and that he has more than his fair share of the good things of the world. As for his spiritual development, I know nothing at all about it. It seems to me that in all fairness his fraud ought not to be allowed to count against him. He was then fifteen or sixteen, and he must now be nearing forty. I've told you this story because you asked me what I knew about him. It does not mean that the person on whose behalf you were enquiring will be at any spiritual risk in his home. I'm very glad in any case that Dominique remembered me and gave my name as a referee. This proves at least that our relationship left some impression on him and that is ultimately a comforting thought. One imagines that one has lost sight of a person or even quarrelled but Lord Jesus holds all the threads in his hand and can relink them if He wills. Who knows if our paths may not cross again for some fruitful purpose?

I don't need to tell you, Reverend Father, how happy I have been to make your acquaintance, if only by telephone. If ever you pass through Paris, please don't hesitate to call, even briefly, on 'Editions Chrétiennes'. You will be able to ascertain for yourself that we are trying to do good work despite our continual material difficulties. Tomorrow I shall arrange for you to be sent a parcel of our most recent books. Please don't thank me: they are copies that have been so badly printed that they are not good enough to be sold in the shops!

With respectful regards from your son in Christ,

Jean Poulignon

We send you herewith the attached ref. no. 2131 CR for addition to dossier 51.

Since you received the above file, our working hypothesis has been overtaken by unforeseen events which eliminate any prospect of making use of 51A either in the long or the short term.

If, after a preliminary reading of the dossier, you gain the impression that it does not contain information likely to lead to any other positive conclusions, we urge you to return it to us forthwith without troubling to make a detailed diagnosis. We should be happy to have your conclusions by word of mouth as we are anxious to save you from employing your time unproductively.

1 enclosure

Date: 12.7.1968
From: Hecate
To: Minerva
Subject: 5353

Classification: TS
Ref. no. 2133 DB

Your memo 2065 LS of 27.3.1968 requested the application of screening procedure 1 to the above-mentioned agent, including her immediate family circle.

The standard machinery was set in action on 1.4.1968.

In our memo 2114 KR of 17.5.1968 we reported that no evidence of a suspicious nature concerning the above-mentioned subject had been discovered.

The screening process was continued until 1.7.1968 with the same negative result.

Direct contact, as laid down for every screening procedure 1, was not in this case attempted by reason of the fact that it had already previously been made by Hecate 2 whilst carrying out screening procedure 3 as requested in your memo 2023 LS of 11.12.1967.

The favourable outcome of screening procedure 1 in no way invalidates the reservations which we were led to make after concluding procedure 3 (vide our memo 2044 KP of 10.1.1968). We drew attention at that time to the possibility that 5353 might be a double or triple agent. Procedure 1 has shown that this is not at present the case but does not prove that such an eventuality may not arise at some later date.

As for 5354, you stated in your memo 2074 KG of 18.4.1968: '5353's daughter will be allotted identification number 5354'. You did not further specify *which* of 5353's two daughters was to receive the number 5354. We have assumed that it must be intended to apply to the non-crippled daughter but we must once

307

again ask you to avoid this sort of inaccuracy. 5354's nymphomania seems to us to represent a security risk that in our view goes far beyond the acceptable limit.

In conclusion, we consider that 5353 and 5354 should be used with the greatest possible caution and then only if their collaboration proves absolutely indispensable to the good functioning of our service. In that case we should be kept informed of the relevant operations in order that we may keep the subjects concerned under the strictest observation at every phase.

Date: 15.7.1968   Classification: TS
From: Aesculapius   Ref. no. 2134 KT
To: Minerva
Subject: 51

Dossier 51 was forwarded to us for our diagnosis on 26.6.1968.

The subject had previously been subjected to physiognomical, typological, chirological and graphological analyses. It has not been considered necessary to repeat these analyses.

The attached report has been drawn up by the physiological subsection of Aesculapius by combining the synthesis of the external analyses (vide our report 2048 BB of 12.2.1968) with a consideration of the new information added to the file since our first examination.

Enclosures: one report
            dossier 51 returned

Report

1. 51's Father

We are referring to Lucien Auphal as 51's father for the sake of convenience and also since he acted as such, albeit inadequately, in 51's emotional life.

Information as to Lucien Auphal is sparse. It is not sufficient to allow us to undertake an examination based on a complete life-history nor does it even justify an attempted analysis with a view to formulating any all-embracing hypothesis. Our study of the subject must consequently remain within the narrow limits imposed by the paucity of the biographical details available and we wish to lay stress on the fragmentary and largely hypothetical nature of our attempted interpretation.

It is an indisputable fact that the First World War had a deeply traumatic effect on the subject who was on active service (twice wounded) and lost three of his brothers in this war. His devotion to the memory of his brothers would seem to go beyond the bounds of normal brotherly affection. It is noteworthy that this devotion has lost none of its strength over the years whereas experience shows that the grief caused by the death of someone even closer than a brother or sister (lover, wife or husband) becomes blunted with time. Neurotic fixation is certainly present but we are not able to distinguish between the part played by the ego of the subject and the factor of social pressure which has undoubtedly been very considerable. The social factor itself is resistant to analysis insofar as it is specifically French and its interpretation would require complete familiarity with the psychological and sociological phenomenon known as 'the old soldier'. The importance and persistence of the phenomenon are illustrated by the fate of the subject's two other brothers who after intervals of sixteen and twenty-six years respectively were still adopting social attitudes determined by the historical and emotional impact of the First World War.

Whilst making all necessary reservations as to the specifically French implications of this phenomenon, the fact remains none the less that studies made of our own veterans do suggest certain conclusions applicable, *mutatis mutandis*, to the subject. With certain troops spending long periods continually exposed to danger in the front line, the overwhelming pressure of events brings about a collapse of the personality that may prove irreversible. Physical and nervous exhaustion, perpetual awareness of danger and the permanent spectacle of death create in the front-line soldier an obsessive polarization on the idea of survival. This overwhelming instinct of self-preservation takes over at the expense of other personality factors in such a way as to cause the atrophy of other areas of affectivity. In some cases, this puncturing of the ego turns out to have caused such irretrievable damage to their vital energy that any recovery is out of the question. This produces individuals of enfeebled and apathetic personality, lacking initiative, easily depressed when they become conscious of their psychological weakness, and possessing misanthropic tendencies. They are characterized particularly by their strict social conformism brought about on the one hand by the habit of blind obedience to any orders, however harsh, and on the other by an impoverishment of the personality which leaves a vacuum ready to be filled by domineering social attitudes.

This behaviour pattern seems applicable to the subject insofar as it accounts for his specific characteristics as described by his wife in her posthumous letter: a tendency to depression, a lack of vitality and marked misanthropy. As for his conformism, this is apparent from every single biographical detail contained in the dossier.

We note in the first place that the subject's marriage seems to have been motivated solely by his desire for social integration. His choice of partner is interesting in that it was made in such a way as to exclude any sentimental or even emotional preference.

The subject had recourse to a relatively archaic method of selection in which the responsibility for the choice rests on a third party. It is significant that this third party was a lawyer, a typical representative of the social order.

Similarly, although his wife's adulterous affair soon came to his notice, he did nothing about it, whereas his notorious strictness and puritanism should have led him to do so. He tolerated this liaison because it remained hidden and did not compromise him in the eyes of the world. It is not possible to know if it caused him suffering but we do know that he waited eleven years to get rid of the lover who had by that time become a 'terrorist' and was condemned as such by the existing system of public order in France. It is probable that he would scarcely have decided to liquidate the lover had this political and social justification not reinforced his personal grievances.

As for the subject's relationship with 51, it fits perfectly into the above-mentioned pattern. It must first be pointed out that, being aware of his wife's liaison, the subject must perforce have been aware of the possibility that she might become pregnant and thus could have taken the simple and indeed elementary legal steps necessary to avoid being saddled with an illegitimate child. His passive attitude and his apathy prevented him from doing so, in the same way as his misanthropy found expression at 51's expense from the moment he was born. Later on, any interest shown by the subject towards 51 always stemmed from social pressures: his running away from home, his difficulties at school and his marriage were all events which forced him to adopt the attitude expected of a supposititious father.

The subject's opposition to the marriage between 51 and 51A is in this respect peculiarly significant. In spite of the subject's obvious fanatical attachment to the memory of his brothers whom he considered heroes, he had accepted the idea that a bastard should bear the same name as theirs, and shamefully insinuate himself into the family circle, as long as this intrusion should remain undiscovered. On the other hand, the marriage of his supposed son to a Jewish anarchist was unacceptable in that it publicly compromised the subject in the eyes of the world. Hence the pressure exerted on 51 to make him break off his affair with 51A and his subsequent agreement to the marriage with 52 who conformed to the standards accepted in the subject's social milieu in every respect.

Whatever the subject's motivation may have been and whatever value our attempted interpretation of the facts available to us may or may not have, it is undeniable that 51 was brought up by the subject in an atmosphere that was eminently conducive to neurosis. This atmosphere was made up of wholly negative elements, such as the morbid fixation on the dead brothers, the withdrawal from society whilst bowing to its standards, the arousing of feelings of guilt in the bastard, the desacralization of the wife and mother, deprivation of all paternal affection, various pressures that were crippling inasmuch as they stemmed solely from the dictates of society, all leading to the one major result, namely 51's inability to reach the stage of identification with the parent of the same sex.

2. 51's Mother

It is plain that this subject's emotional life has been dominated by an unresolved father fixation which appears in almost every paragraph of her posthumous letter. The subject's marriage was less the result of maternal pressure than of the subject's unconscious desire to replace her recently deceased father. Here again, the choice of partner is interesting in its exclusion of any element of personal selection; the subject was anxious to replace her father and a father is not *chosen* but *given*. It is significant to find a relatively emancipated subject, living in an open milieu of students, accepting a husband chosen for her by the person whose function (drawing up marriage contracts, wills etc.) is a symbol of the family unit in a patriarchal society. This father-fixation also explains her acceptance of an older husband, with war experience behind him and already established in life, who could more easily be identified with her father.

It is hardly necessary to emphasize the extent to which the principal episodes of the subject's life are conducive to neurosis: her father's traumatic death, the premature decease of her child Lucie, a crippling marital relationship, a surreptitious adulterous affair, a second, illegitimate, child, the murder, indirectly, of her

313

lover by her husband. One can with great probability assume sexual frustration after her lover's death.

The outcome has been a total transfer of the subject's emotional potential to the person of 51. The posthumous letter offers too blatant an illustration of this phenomenon for us to need to devote our time to proving this obvious truth.

On the other hand, it is essential to examine the *manner* in which this phenomenon expresses itself. To do this, we shall select the most critical period of the subject's emotional life, i.e. when she learns that it is her husband who has caused her lover's disappearance. The above period is all the more interesting in that it most probably marks the beginning of the process of massive transference onto 51.

In her posthumous letter, the subject justifies her refusal to leave her husband by various arguments, none of which, as she frankly recognizes, is completely convincing. She admits the possibility of complex psychological reactions, since she goes so far as to draw a parallel between her own attitude and her husband's fixation on his dead brothers and she herself recognizes this fixation as being of a neurotic nature. This attempt at introspection is praiseworthy, but as always, completely inadequate.

We can see four other possible and complementary interpretations of the subject's attitude:

1) The unresolved father-fixation may have played an inhibitory role. Leaving a husband who was the incarnation of her father-image would have been the equivalent of causing her father to die a second time. We must stress that the obvious character differences between the father and the husband in no way hindered such an identification. The subject had been aware of the equivocal nature of her fixation for an irresponsible and fickle father (vide DL VIII, Appendix I, ref. no. 2085 SV: 'I adored him but felt guilty about it. I was like a good girl who's fond of a bad boy.'). It is not unlikely that her guilt-complex found adequate compensation in the character-pattern of her husband, whose strict nature was more in line with the classical image of a pater-familias.

2) Though the available evidence does not justify a diagnosis of neurotic masochism in the subject, it cannot be denied that at the specific moment which concerns us here, one can detect a certain

masochistic behaviour linked with the existence of a guilt complex. The subject was at that time suffering from an acute anxiety complex and obsessed by the idea that her lover had been denounced as a result of her own carelessness. Remaining in the conjugal home, with all the prospective frustration that this would entail, enabled the subject to sublimate her anxiety, since she would be 'paying for' her carelessness.

3) Referring to her husband, the subject wrote: 'Going away and leaving him would have meant breaking with the past in order to start a new life ... Staying with him would mean remaining with the memory of your father.' (DL VIII, Appendix I, ref. no. 2085 SV.) This is a very common psychological reaction. Her adulterous liaison represented for the subject the apex of her love-life and she did not hope for any comparable happiness in the future. She therefore set out to make every effort to keep her memory of it fresh, since the subject plainly had a deep, unconscious fear of her own forgetfulness. This anxiety encouraged her to look for outside help which, in this instance, could only come from her husband. This is not a paradoxical choice because the important thing for the subject was to find additional powerful emotional drive from somewhere and it was a matter of indifference whether this emotional energy was positive or negative. The husband's hatred of the lover represented for the subject an emotional charge far superior, for example, to mere friendship with one of the lover's former comrades. Once again we are presented with a classical psychological mechanism on which it is pointless to expatiate, unless it be to stress the role which devolves unconsciously on 51. Her son, in fact, provided the subject with a guarantee against any predictable progressive diminution in her husband's hatred of her lover. He was in a way the living, nagging reminder for the husband of his marital misfortune and thus would ensure that it would not fade away into forgetfulness. We note on the other hand that after her husband's death the subject found a polarizing substitute activity in charitable work in aid of an association of former deportees and in the macabre photograph permanently pinned on the wall of her bedroom. It was predictable that the delusory fixation on the lover would eventually turn into an aberration. There is probably a direct correlation between this and the subject's alcoholism.

4) While not under-estimating the importance of the three re-actions just described, we believe that they played only a secondary role and that the prime explanation of the subject's attitude lies in the transference of the subject's emotional energy onto 51. The subject's love for 51 cannot be doubted and it is equally undeniable that concern for 51's happiness should logically have led the subject to protect him from the husband's crippling aggressiveness by flight. It is all the more interesting to examine the way in which the subject was able to reconcile her love for 51 with her decision to remain in the marital home. It is in fact a typical case of egocentricity that seems to justify the description of pathological. On three occasions, the subject had suffered an emotional trauma of crippling intensity: death of her father, premature death of her child Lucie, disappearance of her lover in dramatic circumstances. All she has left is 51. In order to keep him, she employed a remarkably efficient technique of impropriation by turning to her advantage her husband's hostility towards 51. Since it was impossible to divert even a part of his emotional potential onto his father, 51 is bound to fix it wholly on his mother. It is also obvious that, deprived of fatherly affection, 51 would compensate by seeking increased affection from his mother. What is more, the hatred shown him by his father justifies the excessive love lavished on him by his mother and will diminish her fear (which is referred to in the posthumous letter) of being an over-possessive mother stifling her son by the weight of excessive love. Whilst the subject herself considers that she is merely compensating or as she herself wrote, 'striking a balance', she is in fact crushing her son. To use a military metaphor we could say that the subject exposed 51 to murderous artillery fire from the husband in order the better to force him to curl up for protection in his mother's trench. This strategy was successfully employed during 51's childhood and adolescence and it still continues to be so now, for it is symptomatic that the subject, conscious that disastrous consequences of the trauma caused by the father's hatred still persist, nevertheless refrains from releasing 51 from them immediately, but confines herself to doing so in a letter (to be opened only after her death) in which she excuses her delay in this most enlightening phrase: 'I shall at least have held on to your love until my dying day' (DL VIII, Appendix I,

ref. no. 2085 SV). We refuse to accept the subject's justification for her delay, which she alleges to have been caused by her fear of seeing 51 side with the deceived husband. In fact 51 has long since come down on his mother's side. The latter is well aware of this, but she has the unconscious fear that 51 may see through her stratagem and blame her for having ensured her own happiness at the expense of his own. This reproach would certainly have objective validity for it is certain that his mother's love has been at least as crippling as his father's hatred – both being in any case inextricably linked – but it would fail to take account of one essential fact, namely that the subject's emotional strategy was planned at an unconscious level and that she never perceived its disastrous implications.

It would be superfluous to list the everyday practices which result from this type of situation (51 was taken into the subject's bed as soon as he woke up, 51's bedroom in his mother's home is kept in order, ready to take him back even though he has been married for a number of years etc.). We shall therefore restrict ourselves to pointing out the continually equivocal nature – not of course realized by the persons concerned – of the mother/son relationship as it appears in the Lindbergh documents.

1) It is symptomatic that, in her posthumous letter, the subject constantly refers to her sexual enjoyment whilst at the same time stating that she wishes to keep away from this delicate subject. This springs no doubt from the desire to ensure that her liaison will continue to survive by transferring the task of remembering it to 51, but her insistence on the sexual aspect suggests that the subject is unconsciously endeavouring to arouse 51's jealousy.

2) The reference to the grandfather's marital escapades was made in the subject's own words: 'almost in spite of myself' (DL VIII, Appendix I, ref. no. 2085 SV), by the use of the technique of automatic writing, a liberating technique inasmuch as it relieves the writer of any moral responsibility. The subject justifies this reference most inadequately and it seems to us to be motivated by her unconscious desire to create an erotic atmosphere between 51 and herself.

3) Still in the posthumous letter, the subject recalls her opposition to 51's marriage to 51A. On this occasion we find a temporary alliance between the couple, whilst on the other hand they both

accept the marriage with 52 as a lesser evil, the father because it satisfied his social conformism, the mother because the lack of strong feelings on 51's part for 52 made her feel less jealous. 'We weren't mistaken' the subject wrote (DL VIII, Appendix I, ref. no. 2085 SV). We emphasize that this is the sole occasion on which the subject associates herself with her husband by the use of 'we'. It is, incidentally, nothing but a typical outburst expressing the subject's negative attitude towards the women surrounding 51 ('surrounded by all those women like wild tigresses . . .' DL VIII, Appendix I, ref. no. 2085 SV).

4) The subject's reference to the sexual practices mentioned by Valérie Rossignat is motivated by the desire, referred to above, to foster an erotic atmosphere in her relationship with 51. It is not unlikely that the subject's obvious satisfaction when dealing with this subject is indicative of suppressed incestuous tendencies.

5) This hypothesis is further supported by the subject's expression of regret that 51 does not tell her about his relations with 52 (relations must clearly refer to sexual relations). It is plain that the subject would like to be the confidante of 51 with regard to subjects that would help to maintain an erotic atmosphere. It may also be supposed that she hoped, unconsciously, that 51's and 52's sexual relations were of a frustrated nature, since any disclosure of this sort would be particularly gratifying in view of her latent incestuous tendencies. The fact that she communicated Valérie Rossignat's letter to 51 so that he might use it as a weapon against 52 shows a mother/son alliance directed against the daughter-in-law.

3. 51

Our lengthy consideration of 51's father and mother enable us substantially to limit the scope of our theoretical analysis of this subject whose case-history is undeniably one of neurosis.

The psychogenesis of homosexuality is complex and dependent on mechanisms that are subtle, varied and intricate. It is however generally admitted that its essential determining factors are an unresolved Oedipus fixation and fear of castration by the father. Sexual equilibrium presupposes a period of desire for identification with the parent of the same sex that the subject has in this

318

case never been able to achieve. It would not be without interest to investigate more closely the constituent elements and stages of the subject's homosexual psychogenesis and more particularly to examine whether it was not a guilt complex towards the father ('children always know' etc.) which in this case provided one of the mainsprings (very often the prime factor is not homosexuality but a guilt-complex which seeks a secondary justification in homosexuality), but such an investigation would have purely academic interest. The numerous details of a biographical or other nature that we possess concerning the subject enable us to omit this stage and examine the fact itself without further ado.

We shall proceed chronologically but for the purpose of clarity we have grouped our observations under five episodes, each supported by one or more essential documents.

A) THE INVENTED CONVERSION

When in his letter 2131 CR the writer describes this episode, he interprets the deceit practised by the subject as being an attempt at social integration.

It is true that there is ample evidence to suggest that the subject is an unstable boy beset by difficulties of communication. This is the result of the feeling of *otherness* of the homosexual, even the suppressed homosexual, which makes him a typical solipsist. But the invention of the conversion takes on a meaning both broader and more precise in the light of further analysis. We have here a manifestation of the latent homosexuality of the subject who transposes his desire to seduce into an imaginary attempt at conversion. It is possible that there may have been some basis of truth in the person of the holiday companion. This is a matter of relative unimportance since the essential issue is that the subject accepted his homosexual leanings by cloaking them in a particularly harmless and even acceptable and reassuring form, i.e. conversion. We can see in this the equivalent of the 'pleasure without sin' which is sought and found in a dream. It is a pity that it was not possible to include the subject's report in the file. We should probably have found in it the typical stages of a process of seduction culminating on Easter Sunday in sexual union through the mediation of the Eucharist. We consider this episode as most revealing of the subterfuges employed by the unconscious to achieve 'pleasure without sin'.

B) ATTEMPTS AT HETEROSEXUALITY

On this point we possess only fragmentary information. From the file it appears that, up till now, 51 has had a relationship of a heterosexual nature with five subjects: Patricia X, Jacqueline X, Valérie Rossignat, 51A and 52. It is of course always possible that 51 has had other heterosexual affairs but the fact is that there is no trace of them in the file and, specifically, no trace in the Lindbergh documents. These last documents reveal without any possible doubt an exclusively masculine tendency. In the descriptive list of objects kept by the subject in his mother's home (DL VIII, Appendix III, ref. no. 2088 MO) there is nothing remotely associated with a feminine friendship or liaison: everything in it is strictly masculine. The same thing applies to the descriptive list 2090 DB (DL VIII, Appendix IV) in which various documents issued by male organizations are catalogued (French Scouts, sports club, army etc.). It is even more revealing that every single letter kept by the subject is, without exception, a letter from a man (DL VII, Appendix VI, ref. no. 2096 KD). In sum, in the whole of the Lindbergh documents, there are only three which appear to be exceptions to the rule and closer examination leads one to make serious reservations as to whether they are in fact basically heterosexual.

The first is a poem dated Oct. 18th 1948 and dedicated by the subject, then aged seventeen, to a certain Jacqueline X (DL VIII, Appendix V, ref. no. 2095 CV). On our first reading of the file we hesitated as to whether to forward this piece of verse to Apollo to discover if the subject had not copied the text from some anthology. However, quite apart from the poor quality of the verse, further examination disclosed a spelling mistake which confirmed us in our belief that the subject was in fact its author. The poem testifies to the existence of a love-relationship but allows no assumption to be made as to whether sexual intercourse took place. The images employed by the subject in the second verse to sing the praises of his loved one are very symptomatic of his homosexual impulses: 'Roman legionary', 'Greek hoplite', 'cabin-boy beloved by sailors'; in each case, there is a transposition into the realm of masculinity, which is set up as an ideal; the homosexuality of the third metaphor is particularly blatant. It would moreover be impossible, without the dedication, to think of the poem as being addressed to anyone other than a boy. Nor would we exclude this last hypothesis, in which case the subject added a fictitious dedication to cover himself should his poem fall into the hands of a third party.

The second document is the text in which the subject relates his memories of an Irish girl, Patricia X, whom he met whilst on a visit to Scotland (DL VIII, Appendix V, ref. no. 2094 KE). It seems quite certain that the subject did not have complete sexual intercourse with her. One sentence of the text is worthy of comment, concerning the parting of the two young people. The subject wrote: 'I was waiting almost impatiently for you to go so that I might indulge in my thoughts of you and of your love for me.' This attitude may be described as angelism inasmuch as the subject prefers an imaginary to a real love-relationship ('I was waiting almost impatiently for you to go . . .'), and narcissism is also plainly present (' . . . and your love for me'). It is well known of course that angelism and narcissism are typical homosexual attributes.

The third document is Valérie Rossignat's letter which was intercepted by the subject's mother (DL VIII, Appendix II, ref. no. 2086 GB). It provides evidence of complete and apparently satisfactory sexual intercourse but without any emotional commitment, if we are to judge by the tone which the writer adopts. Some sentences (e.g. 'because after all, Dominouche, without wishing to offend you . . .'; 'you know old Philippe, he's not the sort to go about crowing . . .') even suggest that the writer of the letter has retained a somewhat lukewarm impression of 51's sexual powers and that her comforting assurances as to the subject's virility ('I protest! I protest!') have as their main purpose to soften the impact of 51A's depressing accusations on this point. However this may be, we consider that the subject's liaison with Valérie Rossignat was an attempt at heterosexuality such as is often found with homosexuals, above all latent homosexuals. It was certainly made easier by the partner's sexual emancipation. It is possible that this emancipation provided the opportunity for a homosexual union through the mediation of a mistress. We note that the subject became friendly with his mistress's husband and that the sexual act which later took place between 52 and Rossignat did not prevent him from remaining in correspondence with the latter. However, in view of the characteristic sexual permissiveness of the social milieu of the persons concerned, it would be going too far to assume that this is proof positive that the subject was seeking vicarious homosexual union.

In conclusion, the file discloses five heterosexual relationships. Of these five, two did not necessarily lead to full sexual intercourse and are marked by certain homosexual features. The liaison with Valérie Rossignat did involve full and satisfactory sexual intercourse but gives rise to certain reservations. We shall reserve our examination of the case of 51A and 52 until later. On the present evidence, it seems that the small number and specific features of the subject's heterosexual affairs, as revealed by our investigation, may be considered as indicative of an inhibited sexuality. It is significant that when the subject was under observation for a period of several months at the time he was living alone at Delphi, no trace of a feminine attachment was discovered. Minerva's naïve hopes that an affair might eventuate with his secretary, 56, were disappointed. In a letter dated 28.10.1967 (ref. no. 1994 ZA) the subject, referring to his secretary, wrote: 'As far as her looks go, I suppose one might call her pretty, but I won't go into details for fear of provoking your rather special brand of humour . . .' This platonic description is not intended to placate any possible jealousy on the part of 52, who is described as being entirely ready to treat the matter humorously. In fact, it is the expression of a deep lack of interest in women, because it is a matter of indifference for 51 whether 56 is ugly or pretty: he does not apprehend her as a sexual object at all. When considering the question of her good looks, he is forced to look at her through someone else's eyes ('the heterosexual 'one') and he makes his comment with such detachment ('I suppose one might . . .') that it is impossible not to realize that he is completely uninterested in the whole matter.

C) MILITARY SERVICE

It was predictable that the subject's spell in the army would be most gratifying for his homosexual tendencies. We need not therefore be surprised if letters from former regimental friends are strongly represented amongst the Lindbergh documents.

The essential document from the period of military service is the short story written by the subject at 51A's instigation after his return from Algeria. It should be read with the account of the imaginary conversion in mind, since both represent two comparable examples of an identical phenomenon, whereby the subject unburdens his unconscious through writing in a way which justifies 51A's remarkable intuition as to the therapeutic value of writing as a substitution for 51's problems.

Before undertaking a comprehensive study of this document, let us note the detail of the military cook who exposes his penis and urinates into the soup, a revealing example of penis fixation with masochistic implications and coprophiliac leanings.

The main characters in the short story are officer-cadets (the subject himself had been one) and paratroopers who, at that time, represented the epitome of virility for many Frenchmen.

We are fortunate in possessing the extract from the book 'Histoire du F.L.N.' (DL XIV, ref. no. 2125 Tc), as it makes it easier to separate the truth from the fiction. We see that the victims of the ambush were troops of a service company of the Cherchell O.T.R. and not officer-cadets operating with paratroopers (a fact confirmed by Brauchite's statement in DL XII, ref. no. 2122 Ew). The subject changes this reality by himself taking part in the story (he was an officer-cadet) and by introducing the paratrooper element. The historical facts are distorted in order to make it easier for the subject and his fantasies to be included in the story. So we find the subject not only telling a story but telling the story of himself.

From the very beginning, the subject contrasts the eminently masculine reserve and taciturnity of the paratroopers with the chattiness of the officer-cadets. One senses that the former are lean, muscular and taut, whereas the latter are depicted in unfavourable colours: they are flabby-cheeked and pink, they are bespectacled, they talk through their noses, their food has 'done them good' and they have let out their belts over their paunches (similarly a little later on, we shall be shown a rather drab old captain with pepper-and-salt hair, who significantly continually plays with his wedding ring, an obvious heterosexual symbol).

This contrast leads quite naturally to a most enlightening scene in which every sentence is worth quoting: 'The others [the officer-cadets] were standing in front of him with the expression of gentle envy that you see on the faces of soldiers in the brothels in Bône. They were doubtless thinking that in due course their rank would give them power over men just as simply as money provided them with women to take to bed. But some of them looked rather like the sort of little man at the motor show who looks at the big chromium-plated cars knowing quite well that he'll end up with a Renault. They were the ones who knew that they would never be put in command of paratroops.' The subject identifies himself of course with the staring officer-cadets. Like them, he is looking at the paratroopers with envy, the sexual note being struck by the comparison with soldiers looking at women. But the subject is writing explicitly of women in a brothel because he is ashamed at his action of looking at these men who are equipped with penises, and therefore condemns it by the guilt-ridden reference to prostitutes. He is waiting for the time when his rank 'will give them power over men' although he is afraid that he will not be given command of paratroops. As the latter symbolize virility, this fear reveals the sexual frustration of the subject who falls in the same class as the sort of 'little man' who will not be given paratroops and will have to be satisfied with 'Renaults', symbolizing the poor feminine substitute. Moreover, the paratroopers are in a position which protects them from being homosexually sodomized: their position is described again and again in an obsessional manner: 'with his back to the wall', 'with his back to the warm planks of the hut', 'with his back to the wall, the heat from which he could feel on his back'.

From this point onwards the story revolves round the adventures that befell prisoners who were captured as the result of an ambush. The subject departs from historical truth by limiting the number of prisoners to three whereas there were in fact four. It is also to be noted that the quoted extract gives no hint as to the prisoners' professions. If the subject invented this specific detail, this would be revealing inasmuch as the school-master and the seminarist future priest are the incarnation of two essential pillars (moral law and religious law) of a society that condemns homosexuality. And we witness the mental collapse of the two prisoners whose degradation is most significantly conveyed to us by heterosexual allusions (the cowardly schoolmaster passes round photos of his fiancée, the guards ask the seminarist if he has a 'bird'). The officer-cadets endeavour to save their skins by every possible means, including treachery – their efforts symbolize those of the subject to escape from his homosexuality, and their rejection of their paratrooper comrade is an identification with the subject's wish to deny his virility and its attractions – but they cannot escape rape, which is accomplished in degrading circumstances illustrating the subject's mingled fascination and repulsion towards the homosexual act.

In the last part of the story, the narrator withdraws from the officer-cadets to identify himself with the parachutist himself. It is to be noted that all the details of the third rape and its consequences are imaginary since the account of the interrogation taken from the book 'Histoire du F.L.N.' makes no mention of the escape of any prisoner after castrating his guard. This last rape is not comparable to the other two for its protagonists are outside its pejorative connotations and on the contrary form part of an ideal order of virility, since both are super-males facing each other in equal combat (let us note in passing that for the paratrooper defeat is punished by the torture of being impaled, the symbolic meaning of which it would be otiose to stress). The extremely detailed account of the rape reveals the subject's erotic fantasies. We see an amazing release of inhibitions through writing, during which the subject launches into a detailed description of the longed-for homosexual act, a description which he justifies on the pretext that it is rape, that is to say an unwilling act, and that the over-riding instinct of self-preservation justifies his pretended acceptance of this act ('he let himself fall backwards with his right leg extended sideways and his left leg bent, arching his back . . . ' etc.). After this full and satisfactory intercourse (but guilt-ridden because it was satisfactory), there follows an immediate reaction of repression, illustrated by the account of the castration of the penis, a reassuring gesture motivated by the desire to wipe out what has happened by destroying the homosexual symbol. (The title of the short story, 'The Splinter', is itself symbolic of the intruding penis – rape – and as such received without having been asked for, even though its insertion may have been encouraged; in addition and primarily it is a penis-splinter that must be forcibly pulled out.)

d) RELATIONSHIP WITH 51A

It is possible that the subject's depressed state on his return from Algeria was caused, as 51A believed, by the moral and political problems arising from his recent experiences there.

It is not impossible that there may also have been some depression resulting from his return to civilian life which, in his case, meant being excluded from a gratifying male world and thrown back into the world of heterosexuality. In such a situation it is plain that 51A's value as a refuge for the subject was not inconsiderable. No doubt she was a woman but she was above all a militant woman, that is to say that her main interests lay outside the influence of her femininity and that her principal activities took place within a predominantly male organizational structure. It is quite conceivable, even, that her earlier collaboration with underground F.L.N. agents attracted the subject inasmuch as it placed 51A in a context both military and Algerian for which 51 still entertained nostalgic feelings. Moreover the subject's hatred of the tyrannical authority of the castrating father found a counterpart in 51A's prejudice in favour of 'the down-trodden' – Jews, colonized peoples, etc. (The subject's repulsion for all wrongful forms of violence was at least in part responsible for his reaction after the kidnapping of the Moroccan leader Ben Barka and above all during the time of tension when he realized that 52's father was adopting towards 53 a domineering and authoritarian attitude which reminded him of that of his own father.) Finally, it is certain that 51A's specific characteristics (a Jewess of extremist views) unconsciously reassured the subject inasmuch as they provided an obstacle to marriage and thus removed the danger of being trapped into heterosexuality.

51A indicates that her sexual relations with 51 were full and satisfactory (vide 8848's report no. 2118 BR). They included the practice of sodomy. In our view it is this practice which in fact ensured the success of their sexual relationship, since anal intromission in the course of heterosexual intercourse is the classical outlet for homosexual impulses.

The reason for breaking off such a gratifying liaison lies probably in 51A's insistent attempts to force the subject to come to terms with his personal problems: 51A saw plainly that her lover was being subjected to grave stress which she attributed to an unresolved Oedipus complex combined with a guilt complex vis-à-vis the father. The resulting homosexuality escaped her notice. But the subject had an unconscious intuition of the danger of any attempts which might uncover his homosexual leanings. He first of all resisted 51A's suggestions and then, under increasing pressure, by breaking with 51A he destroyed the mirror which the latter was continually insisting on holding up in front of him, in which he feared that he might see, and consequently be forced to admit, the image of his real ego. The impulsive marriage with 52 can be interpreted as a panic flight on the part of the subject who threw himself almost literally headlong into heterosexuality in order the better to escape – that is to escape himself. This sexually suicidal behaviour is frequently observed and explains most marriages of homosexuals, conscious or not.

The emotional importance of the subject's liaison with 51A is thus undeniably associated with a very real gratification of a homosexual nature. It is not surprising that the subject should cherish the memory of this liaison, since it was with 51A that, at least in the beginning, he came nearest to complete realization of his unconscious desires without having to make any breach in the barrier of his inhibitions – a breach which would clearly have caused him to suffer. As in the examples of release of inhibition through writing which we mentioned above, by sodomizing a heterosexual partner he achieved at least partially 'pleasure without sin'. The fact that 51 keeps a photograph of 51A in his wallet proves that this attachment still lingers on, as is proved a contrario by the various ways (tearing, eyes pierced by a pin), in which the photograph has been mutilated. It is clear that such mutilations, borrowed from magical incantatory rites, represent the subject's vain attempts to free himself from the memory of the homosexual gratification provided by 51A, an obsessive memory which overrides any 'normal' heterosexual conduct as well as inducing a guilt-feeling for which 51A is held responsible.

It is to be regretted that the file provided so little information on 52. The reason for this must be sought in the fact that the enquiry became prematurely concentrated on an exploitation of 52's liaison with 52A. It is however significant that the Lindbergh documents contain very little about 52 and that the various lists do not mention any object or text dealing with her. On the other hand, we refuse to make the slightest deduction from the tone of the letters exchanged between 51 and 52, as experience shows that the tone of letters between married couples is not always indicative of their real feelings. We are equally reluctant to accept 55's speculations on the marital relations of 51 and 52 which are conjectural in that they are not based on exact information. Even 52's extra-marital relations are not necessarily an indication of marital frustration for it is common knowledge that full and satisfactory sexual intercourse in marriage does not exclude extra-marital experience on the part of one or other or both of the partners. The blatantly masochistic practices adopted by 52 with 52A may however be seen as the outcome of marital frustration of a neurotic nature. It is a pity that we do not know if the subject was aware of 52's extra-marital affairs. If so the subject's forbearance would be explained by the frequency with which neurotic and masochistic elements are found unconsciously associated in homosexuals and it might further be interpre ed as a desire for a homosexual union through the mediation of the wife.

We have seen that 51's marriage with 52 was the outcome of a panic flight from 51A. In the subject's case, as in that of many others, it was probably helped by an artificial emotional urge of a sublimatory nature towards a wife as representing a refuge. This epiphenomenon which had the purpose of rationalizing his desire for flight (I love therefore I marry) was not restrained by any inhibiting homosexual mechanism since, at the unconscious level, the absence of any real feelings for 52 was in fact reassuring inasmuch as it implied a limited commitment on the subject's part and encouraged him to think that his ego would remain unscathed by the trap of marriage.

It was unlikely that 52 would reconcile 51 to heterosexuality. Two documents in the file bear witness to her failure and to the persistence of homosexual impulses.

The first was already to be found in the file which was forwarded to Aesculapius on 3.1.1968. It was the postcard representing Labisse's picture *Mythomécanique*. Its description by Apollo is too vivid for us to stress its aesthetic-cum-sexual qualities in the eyes of a suppressed homosexual: a woman seen from the back and thus deprived of her exclusively feminine attributes (the pubis, breasts), a provocative posterior but curved and firm, thus suggesting a male posterior (Apollo himself emphasized the difference between this and the typically feminine posterior of a Rubens or a Renoir), a strongly marked furrow between the buttocks, sharp mountain peaks and tridents obviously symbolizing the penis. This close association of the two essential elements of the picture (the woman's posterior on the one hand, the peaks and tridents on the other) suggest of course the act of sodomy. The subject's enjoyment of the picture was so great that he decided to carry the photographic reproduction about with him (the postcard was cut down in order to fit into his wallet). This decision was not guilt-inducing since the central subject of the work was officially a woman, a reassuring proof of orthodoxy – once again we find the 'pleasure without sin'.

The second document is the letter sent to 53 by 51 on 31.10.1967 (ref. no. 1998 JP). In it the subject tells his son a dream; it is a matter of indifference whether this account was true or imaginary, since its importance is identical in either case. You will recall that it deals with the episode of the concierge of a block of flats who swells up like a balloon and gets caught between two branches of a tree. Its interpretation is simple and illuminating. First the subject makes the person undergo a grotesque change for the worse: she swells up until she ceases to look like a human being. This metamorphosis represents 51's repulsion for any heterosexual object and this results in an unconscious desire to see it disappear: the concierge rises into the air towards the sky. Her husband vainly endeavours to hold her down by her feet, just as the subject spends his time trying to repress his deep impulses and hangs on to heterosexuality while realizing the fruitlessness of his efforts. Then the concierge is caught up in a tree symbolizing the obstacles set up by society. Incidentally, the firemen, who are the product of that society whose orders they carry out, soon arrive to hand back the wife to the husband (impose her on him): it is

329

plainly impossible to escape heterosexual orthodoxy. The subject concludes: 'You must write and tell me quickly if Madame Marcelle is still the same size as ever, or whether she's grown as big as she was in my dream. I keep on wondering all the time and it stops me working.' These two sentences illustrate his anxiety to adapt to orthodoxy by transforming the heterosexual object and making it acceptable by removing its (dreamlike) impression of deformity, thus finally eliminating the inhibitions which dominate his ego (prevent him from working).

But one needs only to re-read our earlier summary of the external analysis devoted to the subject to see how much the latter remains psychologically damaged by his suppressed homosexuality. The expressions used in the summary ('over-riding psychological barriers', 'suppressed inhibitions', 'super-ego', 'inhibitory complex', 'mechanical interpretation based on conventional moral or religious standards' etc.) are explained by the psychological analysis which at the same time provides a new dimension and a more exact significance. Thus we could not find a better conclusion to the present study than the one with which we ended our summary of the external analysis: 'To sum up, the subject has a rich and even involved personality which finds difficulty in accepting its complications and takes refuge from its internal conflicts in emotional reactions of such intensity that they could, in the long run, jeopardize his personality structure by exposing it to dangerous psychological strain.'

4. Exploitation

In memo 2132 GT issued after despatching the file to us, Minerva stated that their working hypothesis had been overtaken by unforeseen events, which excluded any prospect of exploiting 51A.

We should not in any case have found it possible to give support to the proposal. The hypothesis put forward was based on a correct appreciation of 51A's character and skilful manipulation could have made her behave in a way objectively contrary to her opinions, but subjectively gratifying for her romantic activist tendencies. On the other hand it implied a reactivation of the relationship between 51 and 51A that we consider would be very precarious. Up till now the solidity and impermeability of the subject's repressive-inhibitory defence mechanisms had been most seriously under pressure from 51A's attack on them. It was only by sudden retreat that the subject was successful in preserving them. It is as we have explained quite understandable that the subject's memories of his liaison with 51A have remained pleasant ones and that he should have told her this on one occasion when he met her – a chance meeting, we must point out; but we are convinced that he would seek safety in flight from any attempt by 51A to bring him back to her by using the same threats as before.

We would say therefore that close scrutiny of the file has led us to the conclusion that any exploitation of 51 must proceed from the violent destruction of his inhibitory defence mechanism, that is to say by forcing the subject to become aware of his homosexual tendencies. We must stress that the outcome of this will be complete psychological disintegration, the short-term effects of which are at present incalculable. But it is certain that failure to achieve this breach in his defences will enable the subject to continue to evade our clutches since even although his self-imposed control is strictly libidinal in nature, its effect is to provide his overall personality-structure with considerable powers of resistance to any adverse pressure.

It is to be feared that any conventional approach will be doomed to failure since the subject has most probably been exposed to homosexual temptations which he has overcome. Our approach must be thought of not as a single operation (seduction) but a dual one (forced awareness followed by seduction). A conventional approach would require exceptional tact and skill on the part of the agent selected; any false step would be fatal. Its inherent difficulties would moreover entail considerable delays.

We recommend an indirect attack using the element of shock provided by the disclosures contained in the posthumous letter. By avoiding a frontal attack on his latent homosexuality, which is protected by powerful defences, it will enable them to be outflanked by using the traumatic disclosure of his bastardy as a detonator. The subject's psychological universe will thus be gravely undermined and his possibilities of resistance considerably weakened. His ensuing vulnerability must be immediately exploited to force the subject to a realization of his libidinal tendencies in circumstances conducive to his future utilization.

We emphasize that the disclosure of his bastardy and the ensuing seduction must be the work of the same agent. The operation is indeed based on the fact that the subject's problems spring from his failure ever to achieve the stage of wanting to identify with the parent of the same sex. The agent who, by revealing his bastardy, can release the subject from his castrating father, will be thereby endowed with special powers and the emotional charge which the subject was unable to polarize onto his father might be automatically transferred to the man who has castrated the castrating father.

Date: 15.7.1968   Classification: TS
From: Hecate   Ref. no. 2136 WK
To: Minerva
Subject: 8956

In your memo 2108 DA of 9.5.1968 you requested us to examine whether the above-mentioned agent's cover was adequate protection against screening by French security services.

The answer is in the affirmative.

1) Operation DL 51 is to cease forthwith.

2) You will take all necessary steps to ascertain the date of 51's next trip to Paris. We shall need to be informed at least forty-eight hours in advance.

Date: 16.7.1968
From: Minerva
To: Jupiter
Subject: 51

Classification: TS
Ref. no. 2138 SA

Please receive herewith Aesculapius' report 2135 NS on the above-mentioned subject.

Its conclusions seem to us to provide the key to the problem of 51 and we request your authority to set up an operation in accordance with the plan outlined by Aesculapius.

Enclosure: Aesculapius' report

Date: 22.7.1968   Classification: TS
From: Jupiter   Ref. no. J 8414
To: Minerva
Subject: 51

You are hereby authorized to prepare plans for the operation
proposed in your memo 2138 SA of 16.7.1968.

My final consent will depend on the quality of the project you
submit to me and on the way in which it solves the difficulties
raised by the operation.

You are to take the greatest care in your selection of the agent
who will be responsible for approaching the subject and his
subsequent exploitation.

You will ask Aesculapius to provide further elucidation of the
following sentence of their report: 'We must stress that the
outcome of this will be [51's] complete psychological disintegration, the short-term effects of which are at present incalculable.'
What use can a *disintegrated* subject have for us?

Date: 26.7.1968   Classification: TS
From: Minerva   Ref. no. 2139 TQ
To: Jupiter
Subject: 51

In accordance with the request contained in your memo J 8414
of 22.7.1968 please receive herewith an additional memorandum
by Aesculapius, ref. no. 2140 CV.

1 enclosure

By using the expression 'psychological disintegration' we intended to imply that our treatment of the subject will have the effect of radically disturbing the more or less stable equilibrium of his contradictory impulses which he has hitherto succeeded in preserving. In other words, the trauma will be caused by the fact that the subject will be brought harshly face to face with an image of himself that he has been denying since childhood or in any case since adolescence. It would be dangerous to underestimate the gravity of this trauma which will have the immediate effect of completely disorganizing the subject's control system since the psychological mechanism which he has organized and which has till now shown itself to be relatively efficient will no longer be applicable to the completely fresh reality which will face him. During the period before the process of forced readaptation to the new situation has got under way, the subject is liable to react irrationally and irrevocably to his family and to his social and professional circles, thus compromising his career and reducing or even destroying any interest we have in his exploitation. It is difficult to lay down exactly the length of any such period, which is without any doubt the most awkward phase of the operation, but we think that one or two weeks should be sufficient for the subject to accept the new situation and to start adjusting to his social and particularly his family context.

Having made due allowance for these contingencies, we feel it incumbent on us to stress more explicitly than in our report the liberating and thus positive character of the treatment which we

338

propose to apply to the subject. It would be a mistake to interpret the operation as conceived by us as an assault on the subject's personality: we are, on the contrary, concerned to open his eyes to the real truth about himself. If the subject succeeds in overcoming the initial trauma of a complete reassessment of his ego, he will reap substantial benefit from it, since the internal contradictions which at present continually spur him on to exhausting efforts to achieve a precarious equilibrium will be finally resolved. The most positive and durable result will be to free the subject from his present sexual frustration and enable him to achieve an integration of his personality that he has never experienced hitherto. In its first stage the treatment will therefore be a liberating and not a damaging factor and will encourage rather than stunt his development. It is certain that, later on, when it moves on to the exploitation of the subject, the operation will to some extent mitigate his euphoria inasmuch as he will find himself in the position of having to pay for his treatment. We are convinced that the trauma caused by this will be less grave than the initial trauma mentioned above. It must not indeed be forgotten that the subject's present powers of resistance and the rigid behaviour which stems therefrom are closely linked with the repression of his latent homosexuality. The revelation and the acceptance of his homosexuality will lead to a new flexibility in his personality which will render his exploitation easier for the subject himself. In any case, even should this assessment prove too optimistic, the service would merely find itself with a normal situation on its hands which would be amenable to the usual methods of coercion.

5672 reports that 51 and his family left Delphi on 27.7.1968 for
Maupertain where they are spending the month of August.

We note your information concerning the movements of 51 and
his family but would remind you that the instruction contained
in our 2137 IB of 16.7.1968 requested you to give us at least
forty-eight hours' notice.

We note your comment of today's date (ref. no. 2142 GA) but
would remind you that the instructions contained in your 2137
IB of 16.7.1968 requested that you be warned at least forty-eight
hours in advance of any trips made by 52 to *Paris* and not to
Maupertain.

Moreover it is in any case impossible for us to guarantee to give
you forty-eight hours' notice. 5354's dismissal has removed our
only source of intelligence concerning 51's personal or family
movements. 5672's endeavours to approach the Spanish servant
who has replaced 5354 in Delphi have proved abortive. Except
by chance, we cannot therefore see any way in which we could
manage to be warned forty-eight hours in advance of 51's plans.
5672 obtained the information about the journey to Maupertain
through Parthenon channels.

We note that you will not find it possible to guarantee forty-eight hours' notice for 51's *personal* or *family* movements.

We shall consequently rely on you to inform us concerning 51's *professional* movements with the advance notice as requested, specifically by use of the channel of 8274.

Date: 13.8.1968   Classification: TS
From: Minerva   Ref. no. 2145 BH
To: Jupiter
Subject: 51

We beg to submit herewith for your approval the outline plan 2146 VD of Operation Hymen.

Enclosure: plan of Operation Hymen

Operation Hymen
(outline plan)

Objective

The terms of reference of the present project merely require involving 51 in homosexual relations. The question of possible exploitation of this situation will be held in abeyance for the moment and explored in a later report.

The objective may be considered as attained when adequate material (films, photographs, recordings etc.) has been gathered, perhaps even as the result of a single homosexual encounter between 51 and the agent, but the latter will endeavour to create the psychological and physical conditions likely to lead to a more lasting association with the subject.

Conditions

For practical (since it will not be possible for 51 to spend a night away from home in Delphi) as well as for psychological reasons (the subject's greater freedom of action and vulnerability when removed from his family context), the contact will have to be made in Paris.

For these same reasons, the operation must only be undertaken during a trip to Paris when 51 is by himself (i.e. without 52).

Thanks to 8274 it will be possible for us to know in advance when 51 is going to be recalled to report at the Quai d'Orsay. This advance notice will probably be used in an attempt to ensure that 52 stays behind in Delphi but any such attempt must depend on the circumstances prevailing at the time and the methods to be employed cannot be specified at this moment.

345

Means

The theory has already been outlined by Aesculapius.

In practice it cannot be denied that the success of the operation will depend in large measure on the agent entrusted with its execution.

The selection of the above agent was considered at two inter-sectional conferences at which Minerva, Aesculapius and Venus were all represented. At the end of this preliminary survey agreement was reached as to the suitability in principle of three Venus agents: Pylos, Metion and Doros.

In the next stage, these agents underwent tests in conditions approximating as closely as possible to reality. Each was given the usual documentation on their objective, i.e. in this case on 51, after Hecate had undertaken the appropriate deletions and alterations to ensure that no accurate identification of the subject would be possible. For obvious reasons of convenience it had been decided in the course of the preliminary conference that the tests should be conducted on the spot. The agents were therefore informed that their objective was a member of the French diplomatic corps 'en poste' with us. The part of the diplomat was played by Hades, a Venus agent unknown to the other three, who was recalled to Paris especially for this purpose. The contacts made by Pylos, Metion and Doros, in that order, were therefore as authentic as was humanly possible since the three agents were all under the impression that the situation was real and had no idea that it was, in fact, merely a dummy run.

Each of the three attempts was filmed and recorded from beginning to end.

Finally, the representatives of the three sections concerned saw projections of the films and listened to the recordings. It immedi-ately became evident that the agent Doros was not qualified for so complex an operation, the first phase of which in particular (disclosing to the subject his illegitimate birth) requires consider-able skill.

In contrast, the agent Metion was outstanding in the first phase but his intellectual grasp was counterbalanced by a certain physical aggressiveness which led him to proceed to sodomize Hades rather unceremoniously. The specialists from Aesculapius had stated that, while they found it impossible to decide whether in theory the act of sodomy should be committed *on* 51 or, on the contrary, *by* him, on the whole they tended to support the second alternative. The Venus representatives admitted that Metion's normal practice and tastes made him unsuitable for this second course.

Without showing such sureness of touch as Metion in the preliminary phase, Pylos none the less gave an adequate performance. He was particularly brilliant when it came to the actual intercourse, during which he exercised a power of fascination which was obvious even to the heterosexuals who were watching. This was due to his extremely prepossessing appearance and to his most impressive physical equipment. The final choice of the intersectional committee was thus Pylos.

The fourth stage was devoted to the actual training of the selected agent and in particular to working out a theoretical approach for contacting the subject. No directions concerning this critical phase had been given to the three preselected candidates at the time they were being tried out since these tests were designed to gauge their presence of mind and their ability to adapt rapidly to the subject's unpredictable reactions. For the operation itself, however, we considered it preferable to reduce the necessity of improvisation to a minimum by giving Pylos a fairly strong guide-line which would none the less allow him sufficient flexibility to change course in accordance with the subject's unpredictable reactions. The agent Metion collaborated in working out this approach.

Our intention is therefore that Pylos should introduce himself to the subject as the son of a deportee who met the subject's real father in the camp. Pylos will explain that his own father has just died, making certain disclosures on his deathbed. He (Pylos's father) had been a confidant of 51's real father and the latter, just before he died, had told him about his association with 51's mother and the resulting birth of 51. Since he was convinced that his mistress's marriage would break up as soon as she learned who had denounced him to the Gestapo, 51's real father had made Pylos's father swear that he would look after her and her child should he return safely from deportation. Pylos's father gave his word and was firmly determined to keep his promise but had not

347

had the opportunity of doing so because, contrary to his friend's assumption, 51's mother had not asked for divorce, even after learning the circumstances of her lover's arrest at the time of her brother-in-law's trial. All the same, knowing that he was on the point of dying, he had wondered whether he ought not to have contacted 51 to talk to him about his real father and tell him what sort of man he was and how he had died. Though greatly disturbed by these disclosures and his father's scruples, Pylos had at first hesitated to speak to 51 but had finally decided to do so when he realized that in 51's place he would have liked to know the truth about his real parentage.

The attraction of this scheme is that the fact that Pylos is supposed to have only a second-hand knowledge of these events will explain the fragmentary nature of his disclosures regarding 51's family history. In addition, the deliberately romantic details of the story should stimulate the subject's curiosity and thus lead him to ask Pylos a large number of questions. As a result – and the Aesculapius experts consider this the greatest advantage – the initiative in the conversation will fall on the subject and any further development of the relationship will come from 51 rather than vice-versa. This will prevent the first stage from appearing too aggressive (the disclosures will not be forced on 51 by Pylos but *requested* by the former); any hint of aggressiveness would of course be liable to prevent a smooth transition to the next, physical, phase of the operation. And finally Pylos's ostensible motivation – his pretence that he has reached his decision as a result of what he would have liked to happen had he himself been in the subject's place – will in a sense make both of them feel themselves to be accomplices, a feeling strengthened by the fact that since each of them possesses a different and incomplete version of the events they will be able to compare their respective knowledge in an attempt to piece together a full picture. On this point it may be something of a drawback that we do not know the identity of 51's real father, since it would be unlikely that Pylos's father should have failed to disclose to his son the name of his fellow deportee. We considered the possibility of setting up an operation with a view to removing from the safe in which they are deposited the documents mentioned in the letter written by 51's mother but, quite apart from the fact that an operation of this nature would involve technical difficulties (vide memo 2084 BZ of 2.5.1968), it seemed to us preferable for Pylos to pretend that his conscience would not allow him to reveal the name of his real father to 51 until he had got to know him better and could be sure that he would not make any attempt to contact his father's widow and children, since this might cause further suffering so long after the event.

The final stage of our operational planning was devoted to defining 51's possible reactions when faced by Pylos's disclosures and to working out, experimentally, the appropriate counter-measures. The Aesculapius specialists envisaged four possible reactions on 51's part:

1) Sympathetic interest.
2) Stunned bewilderment.
3) Violent excitement and anger.
4) Incredulity.

The first three of these should present no great obstacle to Pylos's moving on to the physical stage of the operation, the first in particular being clearly the most helpful. The fourth would be the least propitious inasmuch as it would be necessary to force the subject to face up to the truth. Pylos ought, however, to be able to accomplish this by the use of certain biographical details that we know might have been familiar to 51's real father (e.g. birth and premature death of his elder sister Lucie, his difficulties at school, including running away from it in 1941-42, his mother's fondness for the Brandenburg concertos etc.). He might also suggest to the subject that he could find proof of his assertions amongst his mother's personal papers.

Pylos undertook a series of twenty-six tests in the course of which Hades, acting the part of 51, assumed the four basic reactions mentioned above and then various combinations of these four reactions. Each test was filmed and recorded and then projected to enable the committee to offer criticisms and suggestions.

In conclusion we consider that all of 51's reactions that are reasonably predictable have been allowed for and that Pylos has been adequately equipped to handle the problems that might

349

thus arise. It is clear that a certain margin of uncertainty remains and must remain whatever care we exercise and however long we spend planning this operation but we think that this margin has been reduced to an absolute minimum.

Date: 20.8.1968
From: Mercury
To: Minerva
Subject: 55

Classification: TS
Ref. no. 2147 BC

8956 reports that 51 and 52 called on him on 13.8.1968. 51 stated that he had come specially from Maupertain at the request of 55's parents to find out more about 55's disappearance. He adopted an almost threatening attitude towards 8956, even going so far as to talk of the white slave traffic and hinting that if 55 were not discovered soon he would make use of his influential police connexions. 8956 assured him that he did not know why 55 had left him or where she had gone (which is incidentally the truth). 51 warned 8956 that he would soon be hearing from him again.

The following day, 14.8.1968, 52 came back by herself. She showed herself much more conciliatory than her husband and had a long chat with 8956, ostensibly with the purpose of discovering some detail that might put them on 55's track, but 8956 gained the impression that most of all she wanted to discover if 55 had revealed any secrets concerning her own life. He gave her what reassurance he could and they parted on very good terms. Questioned by 8956, 52 stated that she did not imagine that her husband would go so far as to go to the police, since 55 was over twenty-one and free to do as she liked. However, in view of the possible danger we consider that it would be better to recall 8956 forthwith.

Date: 20.8.1968   Classification: TS
From: Minerva   Ref. no. 2148 DM
To: Mercury
Subject: 55

In confirmation of our telephone conversation, we inform you
that, since 8956 has nothing to fear from any security check by
the French police, he is to remain in Paris until further notice.

Date: 23.8.1968   Classification: TS
From: Jupiter   Ref. no. J 7517
To: Minerva
Subject: Operation Hymen

I have examined the outline plan of Operation Hymen. It seems to me satisfactory except for two details. I should like to know:

1) the methods proposed to ensure that 52 remains behind in Delphi during 51's visit to Paris.

2) the methods proposed to enable the association between Pylos and 51 to be pursued in Delphi.

It had not escaped our notice that 52 was liable on the one hand to hold up the execution of Operation Hymen by going to Paris with 51 and on the other hand to compromise its further success by preventing the association between Pylos and 51 from being pursued in Delphi. We had held over the subsidiary question of 52's presence in Delphi for later consideration once you had given your approval of the Hymen project but we think that we have already reached a solution of this problem.

We enclose herewith memo 2147 BC dated 20.8.1968 from Mercury, which suggests that 52 is apprehensive as to whether 55 may have confided in 8956 information as to her (52's) extra-marital affairs. It is thus undoubtedly true that any threat to send 51 the material which we acquired through Operation Justine (photographs and recordings of sexual intercourse between 52 and 52A) would enable us to bring 52 completely under control.

We propose to send to Delphi forthwith an agent whose task will be to engage in sexual intercourse with 52. We recommend Metion for this purpose since his sexual ambivalence has enabled him to achieve successful heterosexual as well as homosexual conquests. Metion will be instructed to achieve his objective – 52's neutralization – with the greatest possible economy of means since it would be better to hold the Justine material in reserve, as it may prove of long-term value. He will however be authorized to utilize this material in the last resort. We consider that we can thus eliminate in one operation the problem raised

354

by 52, not only as far as Pylos's contact with 51 in Paris is concerned, but also as for the possibility of pursuing their association in Delphi.

When we are sure that 51 is irretrievably under control, it will no doubt prove desirable to replace our dual control of 51 and 52, which might prove a source of complication, by a single control of the two of them. This aim would be achieved by replacing the quadripartite association of Pylos/51 and Metion/52 by a quadripartite association Pylos/51/Metion/52. It is with this in mind that we recommend the choice of the agent Metion. The latter has, in fact, shown great enthusiasm for the Hymen operation and he was deeply disappointed to be passed over in favour of Pylos. It is certain that he will try harder than any other possible candidate to bring to fruition any operation which will eventually lead to his working in direct contact with 51.

1 enclosure

Date: 30.8.1968
From: Jupiter
To: Minerva
Subject: Operation Hymen

Classification: TS
Ref. no. J 9710

I accept your plan for Operation Hymen. It is to be put into
effect on the earliest possible date.

Date: 18.9.1968   Classification: TS
From: Venus   Ref. no. 2150 VD
To: Minerva
Subject: 52

Metion reports that 52 is under control. It did not prove necessary to use the Justine material.

Date: 4.10.1968
From: Mercury
To: Minerva
Subject: 51

Classification: TS
Ref. no. 2151 MM

8274 informs us that 51 has been called to the Quai d'Orsay on
14.10.1968 to take part in the conversations with the President
of the Republic of Mauretania. These conversations are due to
be held between 16.10.1968 and 19.10.1968 inclusive.

Date: 4.10.1968　　　　　　　　　Classification: TS
From: Minerva　　　　　　　　　　Ref. no. 2152 GU
To: Venus
Subject: Operation Hymen

Inform Pylos that circumstances suitable for carrying out
Operation Hymen will exist as from 14.10.1968 until 19.10.1968
inclusive.

Warn Metion that 52 must be successfully neutralized during
the above-mentioned period.

Date: 18.10.1968   Classification: TS
From: Venus   Ref. no. 2153 VT
To: Minerva
Subject: Operation Hymen

Pylos has reported by W/T that the above-mentioned operation
was successfully accomplished in the night of 17.10.1968 in
circumstances that promise well for future exploitation.

Pylos will leave Paris on 20.10.1968 to make his report in
person.

Date: 19.10.1968
From: Mercury
To: Minerva
Subject: 51

Classification: TS
Ref. no. 2154 GD

51 is dead.

He died in a road accident on 18.10.1968 at about 1000 hrs, roughly at the time of the opening of a conference at the Ministry of Foreign Affairs at which he was expected to be present. He was driving a Peugeot 404 which he had hired in Paris twenty minutes before. His intended destination is not known. He was alone in the car. The Peugeot left the road about 500 yards from the exit of the Autoroute de l'Ouest, going towards Versailles, and it struck a pylon in the central dividing strip at full speed after knocking down the protective barrier. 51 was killed instantly.

According to the Paris press, the inquest was unable to discover the cause of the accident. The road surface was dry. There was no trace of any mechanical failure. There were no brake-marks. It is assumed that 51 was taken suddenly ill.

Date: 23.10.1968   Classification: TS
From: Vulcan   Ref. no. 2155 BQ
To: Minerva
Subject: Operation Justine

Mars sent us for examination the listening and recording equipment which failed to operate during the above operation.

It is a vibration-triggered VP 405 (modification 212) no. 1428, first brought into service on 1.5.1965. Delivery was taken by Mars on form 24 BS dated 3.7.1965. We have never had any trouble with our VO 405s (modification 212) and we cannot understand why model no. 1428 failed to function since all its parts are in perfect working order. *The failure was probably due to faulty installation.*

Copy for information to Mars

Penguinews *and*
Penguins in Print

Every month we issue an illustrated magazine, *Penguinews*. It's a lively guide to all the latest Penguins, Pelicans and Puffins, and always contains an article on a major Penguin author, plus other features of contemporary interest.

Penguinews is supplemented by *Penguin in Print*, a complete list of all the available Penguin titles – there are now over four thousand!

The cost is no more than the postage; so why not write for a free copy of this month's *Penguinews*? And if you'd like both publications sent for a year, just send us a cheque or a postal order for 30p (if you live in the United Kingdom) or 60p (if you live elsewhere), and we'll put you on our mailing list.

Dept EP, Penguin Books Ltd,
Harmondsworth, Middlesex

Note: *Penguinews* and *Penguins in Print*
are not available in the U.S.A. or Canada

Emma Lathen

When In Greece

The Sloan Guaranty Trust, the world's third largest bank, invested in a hydroelectric project in the Greek mountains.

During the Colonels' coup the Sloan's representative, Ken Nicholls, gets arrested at Salonika railway station.

A second Sloan man, Everett Gabler, is sent to retrieve him – but hasn't a chance: he is arrested too, within hours of his arrival and in broad daylight.

Against all advice, John Putman Thatcher, the bank's vice-president, sets out for Greece and, with the help of two female archaeologists, pulls off the biggest coup of all . . .

Not for sale in the U.S.A.

Len Deighton

Horse Under Water

The depths of perfidy are sounded in this taut, technical story of
a bid to back a revolution with counterfeit money lying in a
a sunken German U-boat.

'I had a sneaking feeling I was breaking the Official Secrets Act
every time I opened this book' – *Daily Express*

'James Bond's most serious rival . . . Deighton decorates his
thrilling plot with equally enthralling detail about secret service
routine' – *Queen*

'This secret service thriller will be read; so will the next and the
next' – Donald McLachlan in the *Sunday Telegraph*

Billion-Dollar Brain

The chilling story of an anti-Communist espionage network,
owned by a fanatical Texan millionaire and run by a vast
computer complex.

'The best thing Mr Deighton has done, a dazzlingly intelligent
and subtle performance which will delight admirers and should
convert those who in the past have found him too complex. Mr
Deighton is really a poet of the spy story, fascinated by the way
things work – not just poison needles and fountain pen signals,
but the details of communication systems, the origins of virus
growths. This book puts him, with John le Carré, so far in front
of other writers in the field of the pure spy thriller that they are
not even in sight' – Julian Symons in the *Sunday Times*

Also available:

Funeral In Berlin

Not for sale in the U.S.A.

John Le Carré

A Murder of Quality

George Smiley, the cleverest and most self-effacing man in Security, investigates a murder in one of England's leading public schools – a murder that was forecast by the victim.

'A book of superb quality . . . If he continues at this level, he will soar beyond any of the great names of this century' – E. D. O'Brien in the *Illustrated London News*

Call For the Dead

It 'makes most cloak-and-dagger stuff taste of cardboard' – as Nicholas Blake wrote in the *Sunday Telegraph* about this spine chiller by the author of *The Spy Who Came In From The Cold*.

Not for sale in the U.S.A.

Clark Sr

The Case of Torches

Just a case of torches – that's all there is missing when Nicky
Mahoun, investigating accountant to a large industrial combine,
starts his inquiries. But the research chemist with Communist
leanings, whose report on the quality of the torches can influence
the placing of a major contract, has also disappeared. Neither
his chronically jealous wife, not his mistress, the fascinating
Valerie Brown, have seen him for days.

Mahoun's investigations are carried out in defiance of his
superiors against a background of boardroom politics, where
power is the prize and the in-fighting is traditionally non-physical.
But violence intrudes: pathetic suicide and brutal murder. Before
the joker is revealed in this pack of scheming executives, Mahoun
faces acute danger, and is made to face questions about himself
and the ethics of a way of life he has accepted, until the catalyst
provided by . . . a case of torches.

Not for sale in the U.S.A.